Modern Guitar Anthems BlackBook

Twenty-nine songs arranged for Guitar Tablature Vocal.

Published 2003
© International Music Publications Limited
Griffin House, 161 Hammersmith Road, London, W6 8BS, England

Editorial, new arrangements and new engraving by Artemis Music Limited

Contents

All My Life

Words and Music by David Grohl, Nate Mendel, Taylor Hawkins and Christopher Shiflett

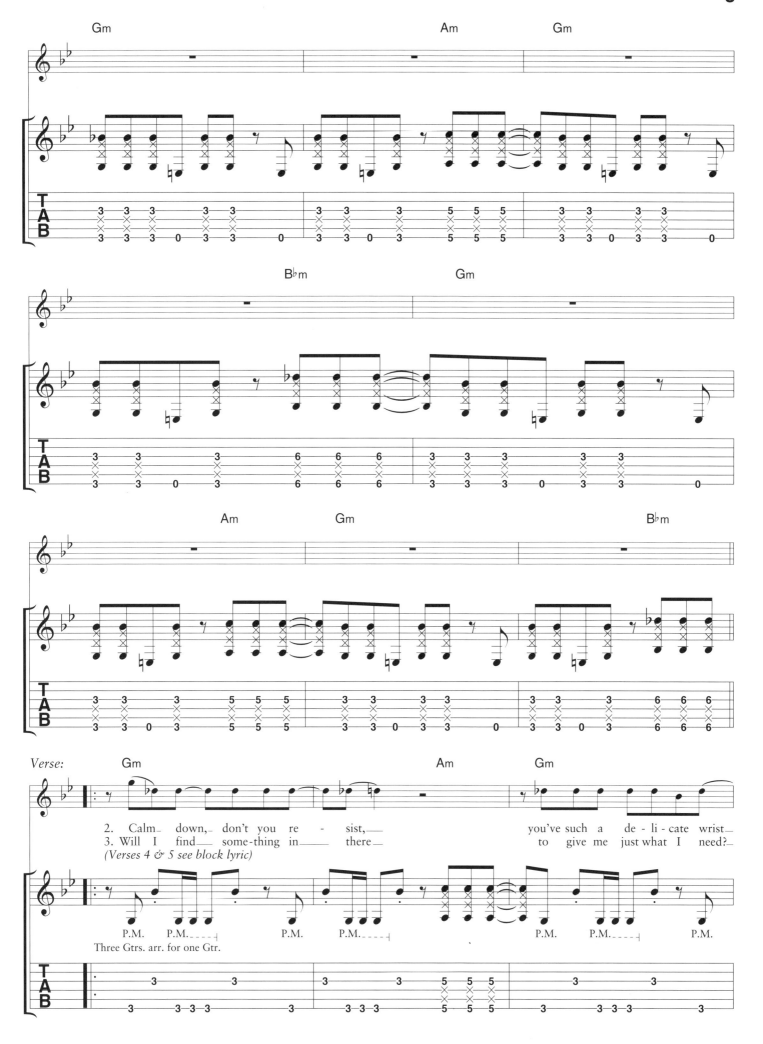

Verse:

2. Calm down, don't you re - sist, you've such a de - li - cate wrist
3. Will I find some-thing in there to give me just what I need?
(Verses 4 & 5 see block lyric)

Three Gtrs. arr. for one Gtr.

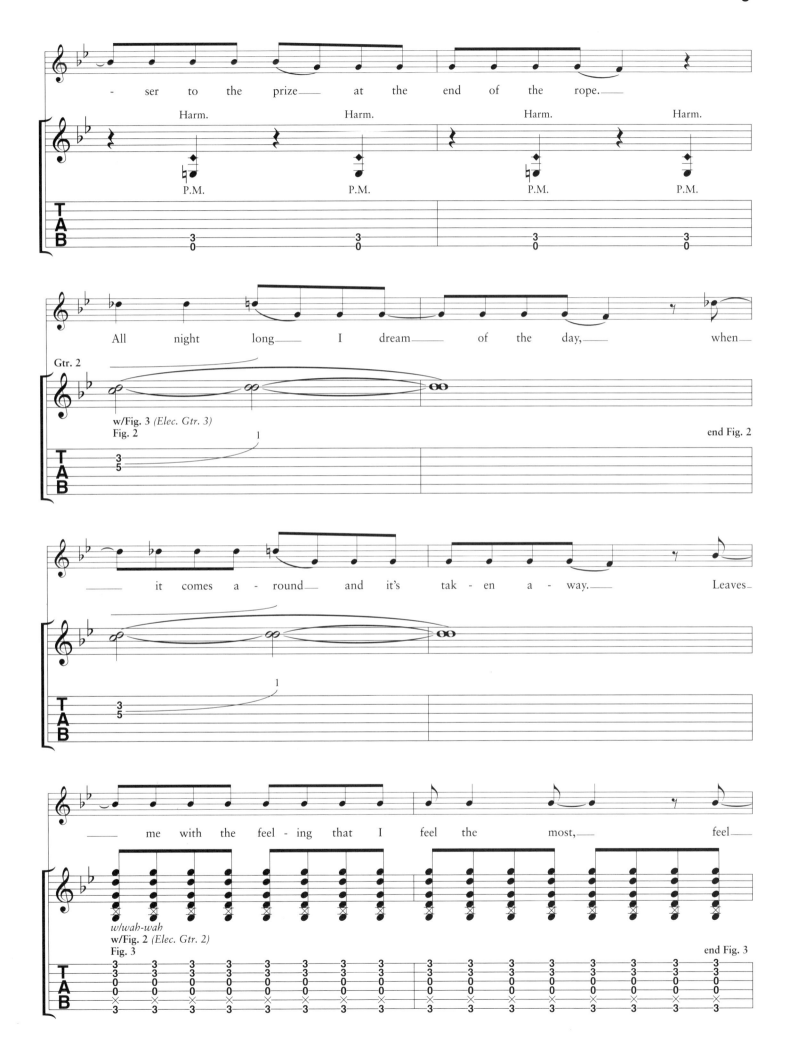

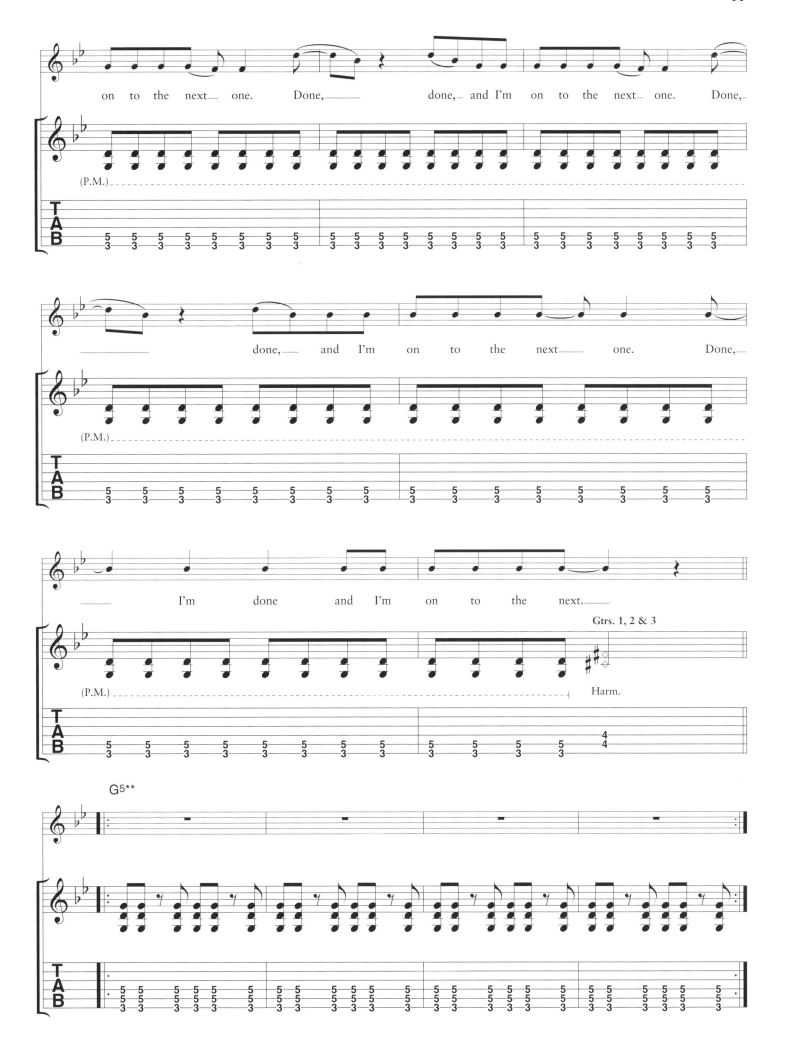

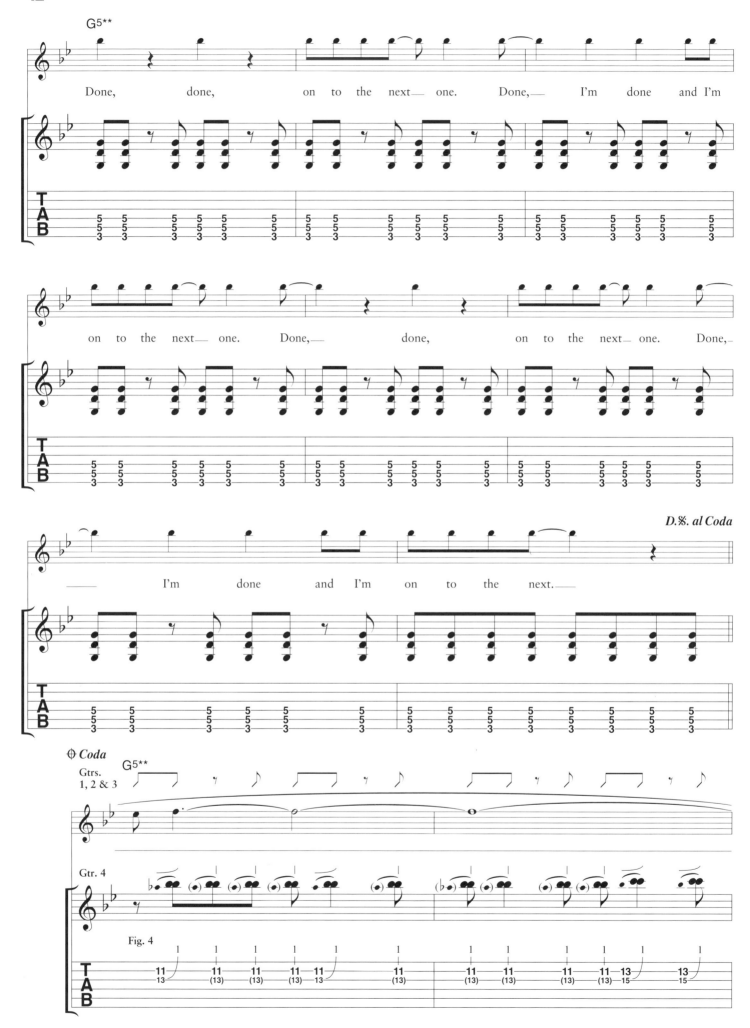

end Fig. 4

Gtrs. 1, 2 & 3

Done, done, on to the next— one. Done,— I'm done, and I'm

w/Fig. 4 *(Elec. Gtr. 4)*

on to the next.——

Verse 4:
Will I find a believer
Another one who believes
Another one to deceive
Over and over down on my knees.

Verse 5:
If I get any closer
And if you open up wide
And if you let me inside
On and on I got nothing to hide
On and on I got nothing to hide.

Believe

Words and Music by Mike Wengren, Dan Donegan, David Draiman and Steve Kmak

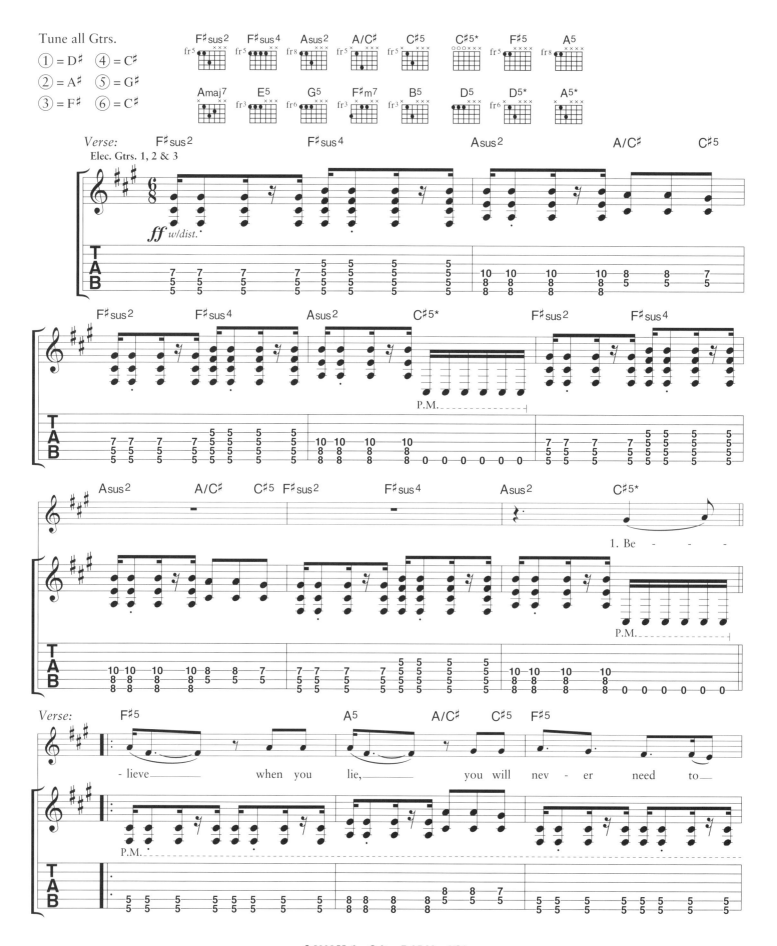

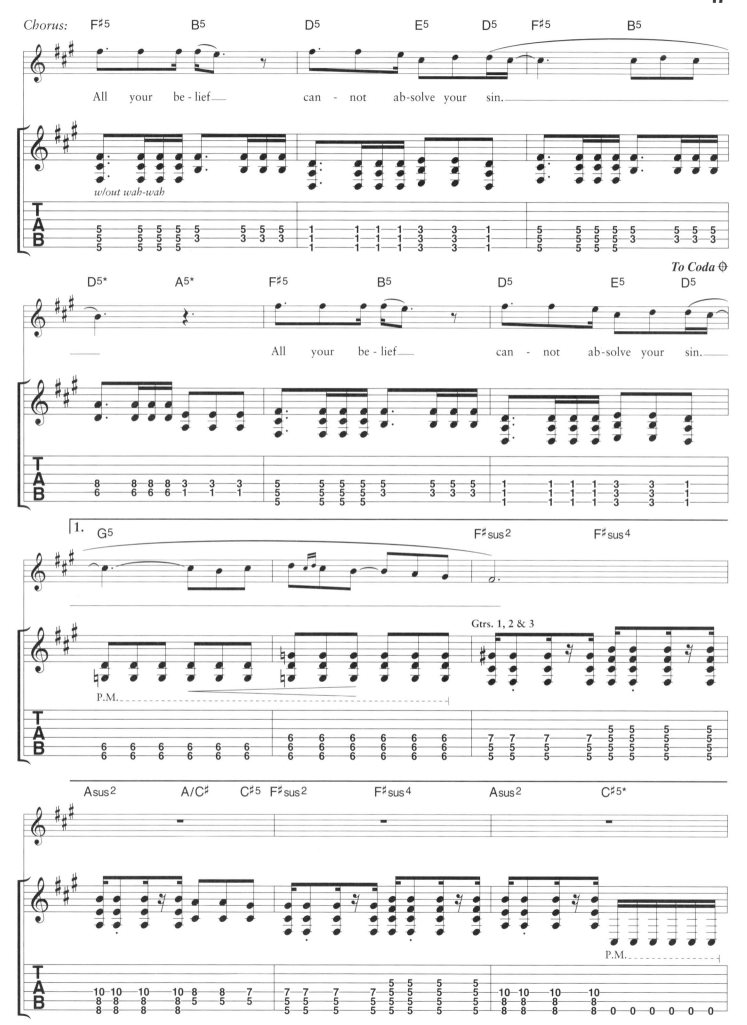

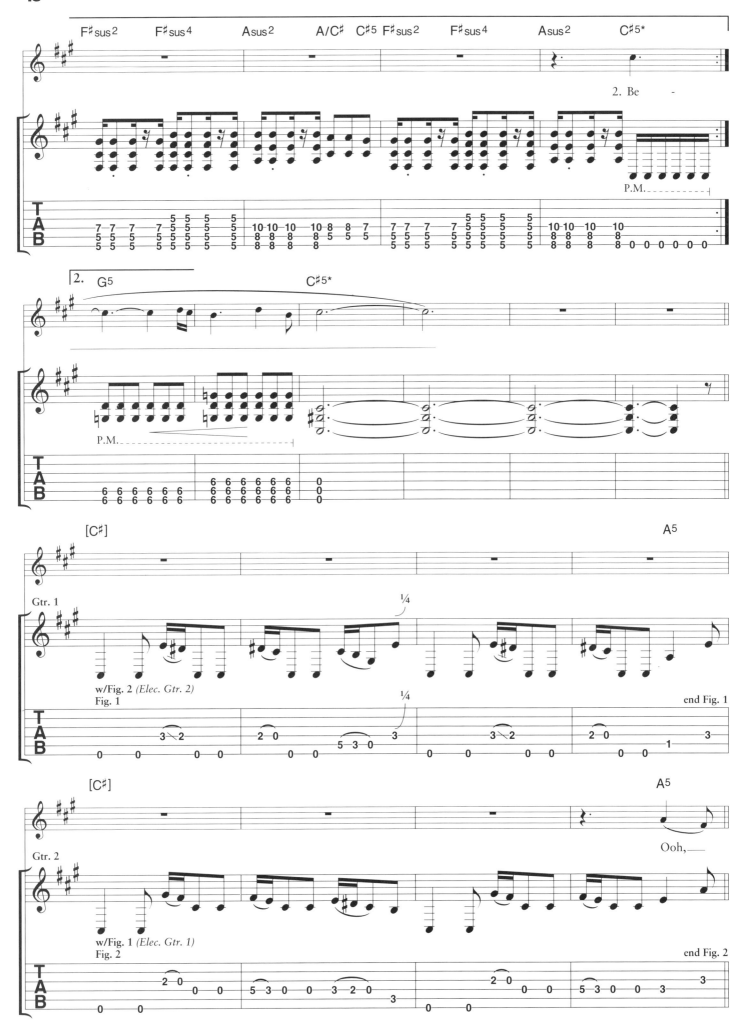

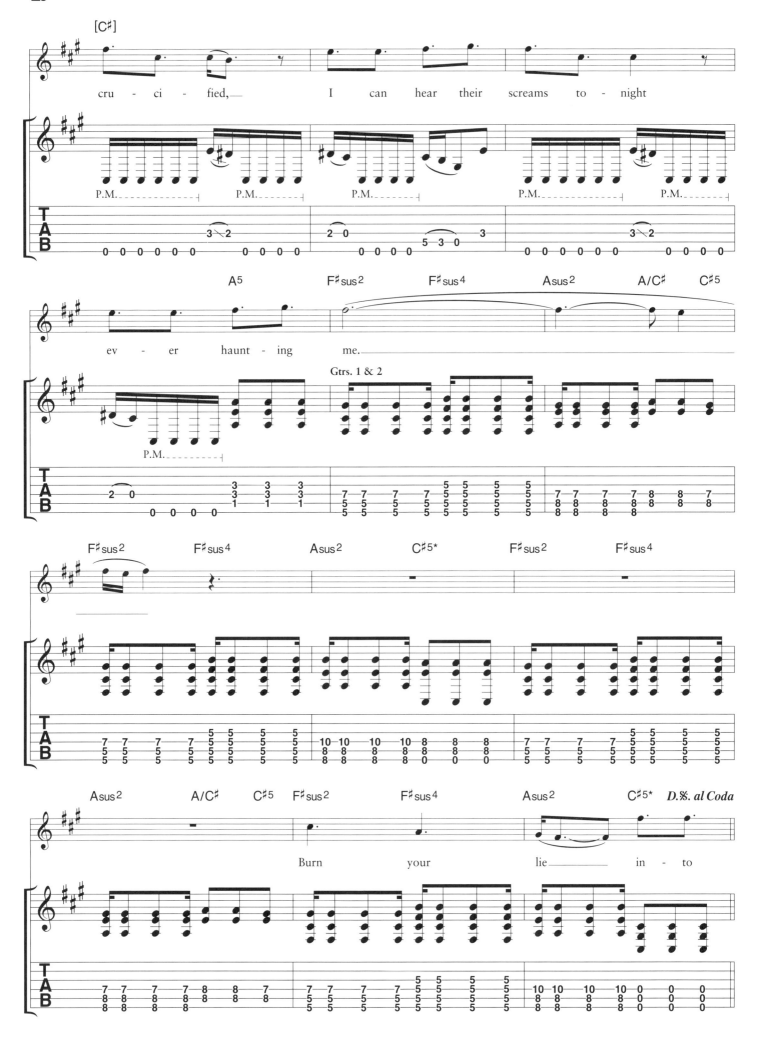

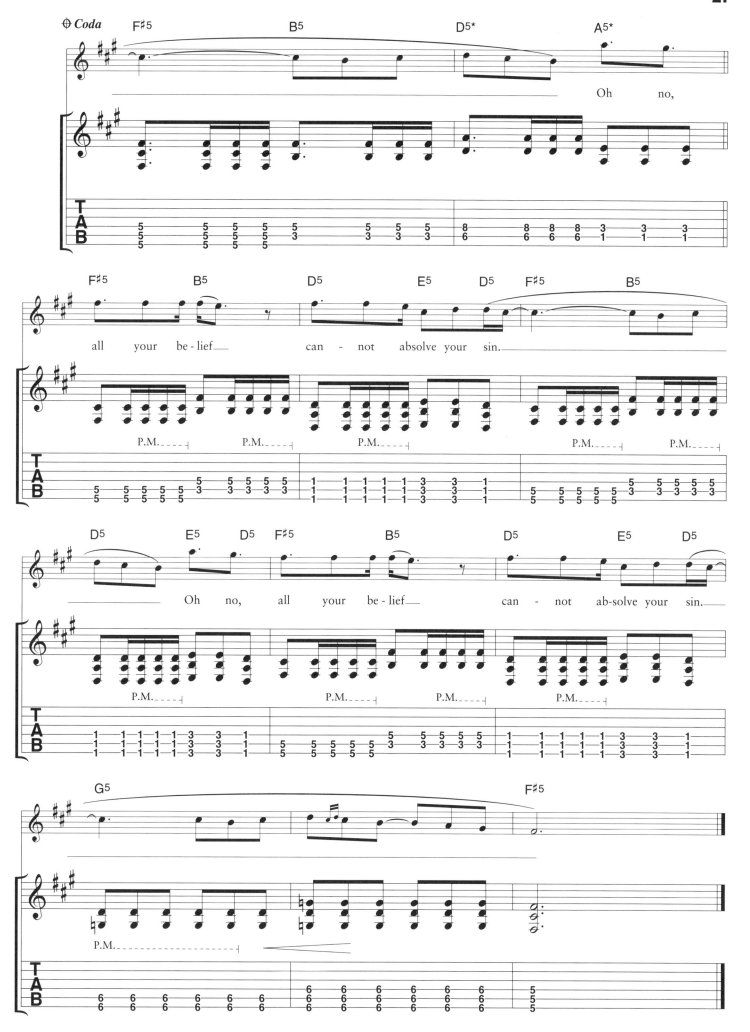

All Over Me

Words and Music by David Williams, Michael Luce, Christian Pierce and Stephen Benton

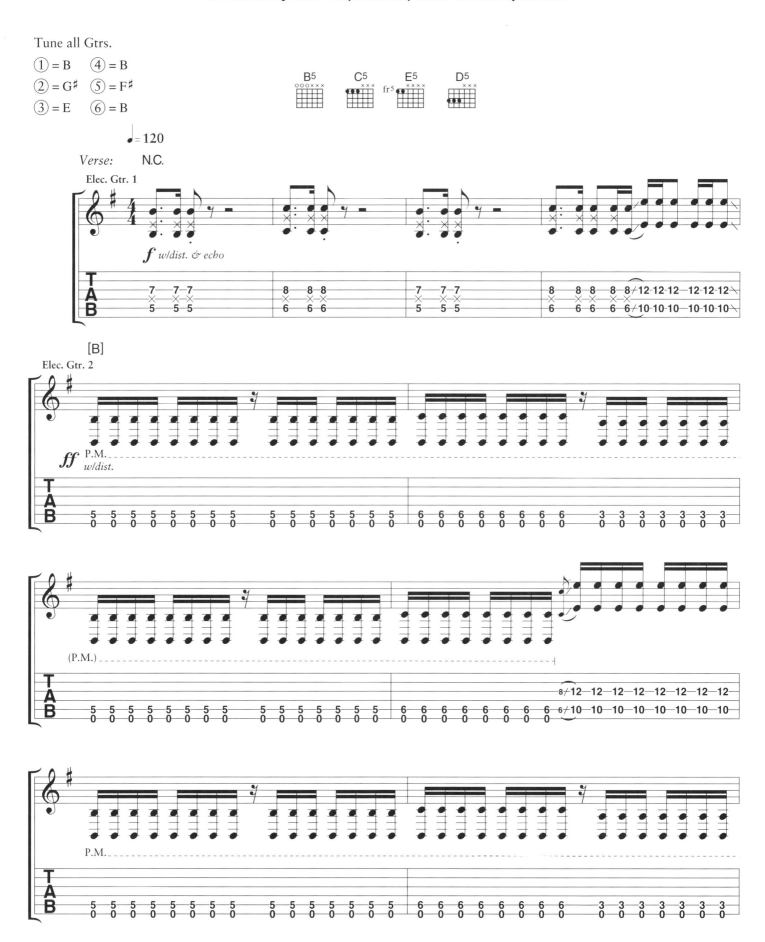

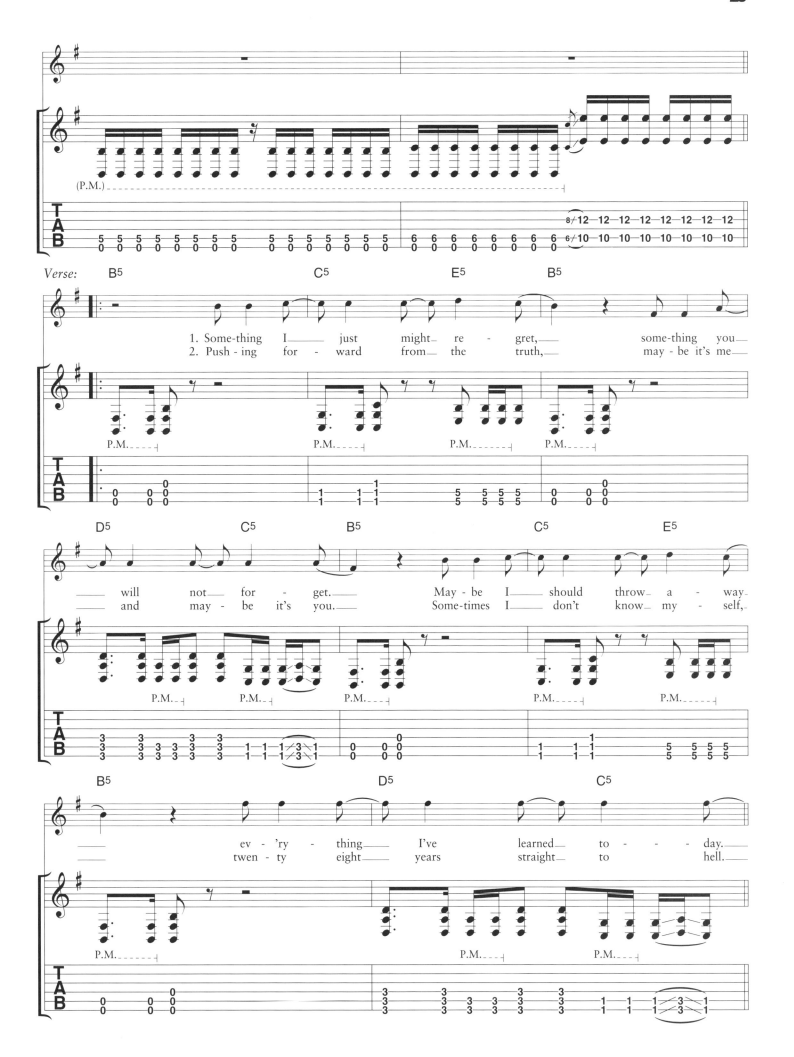

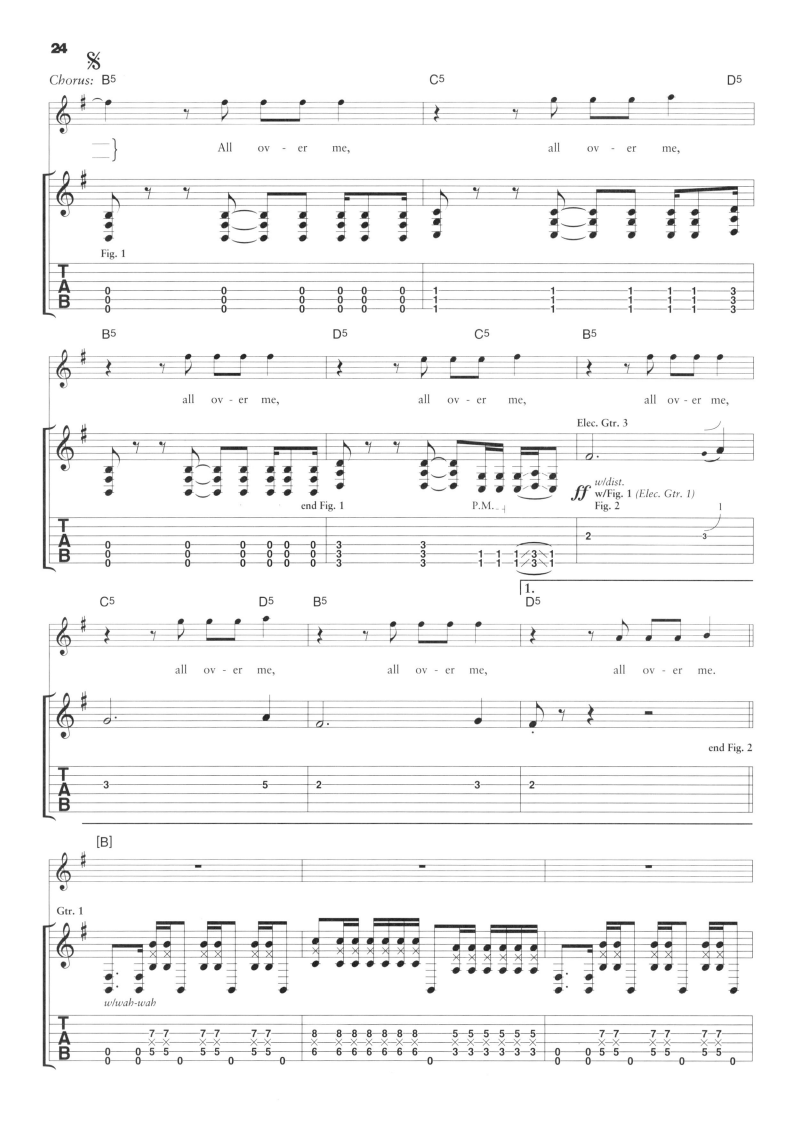

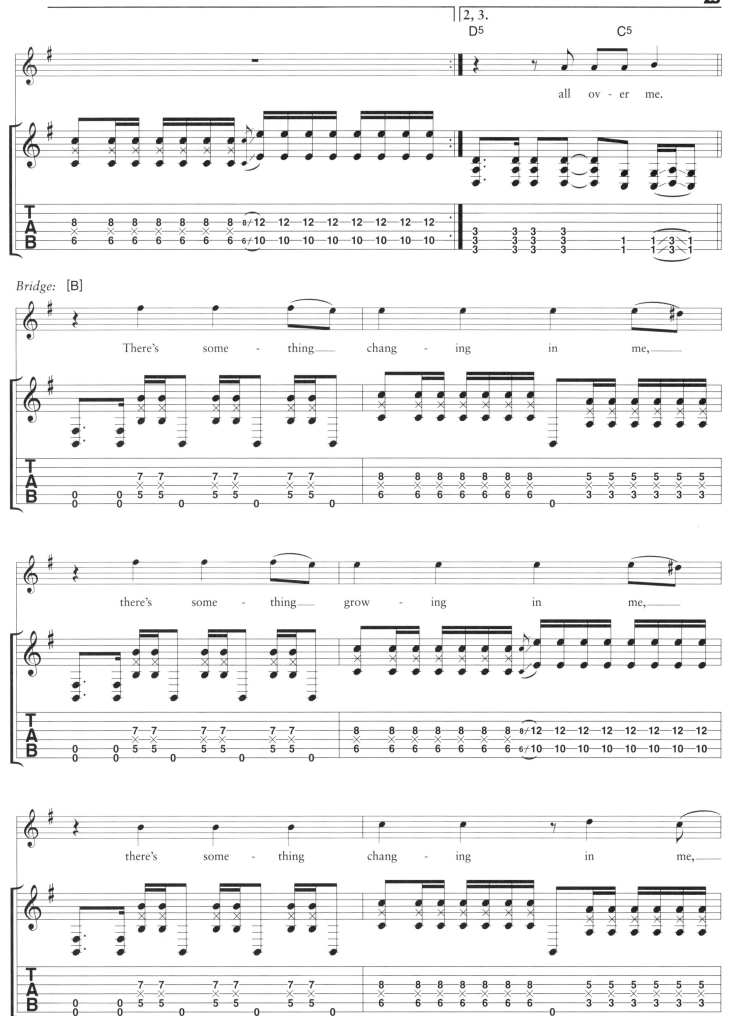

Bridge: [B]

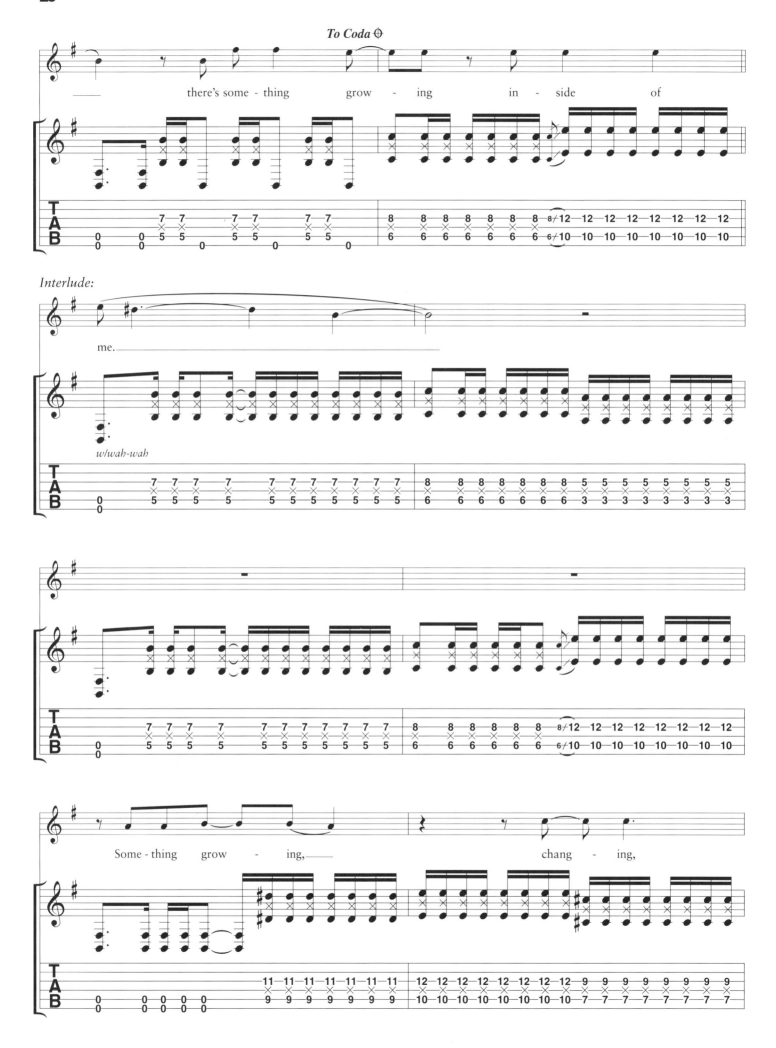

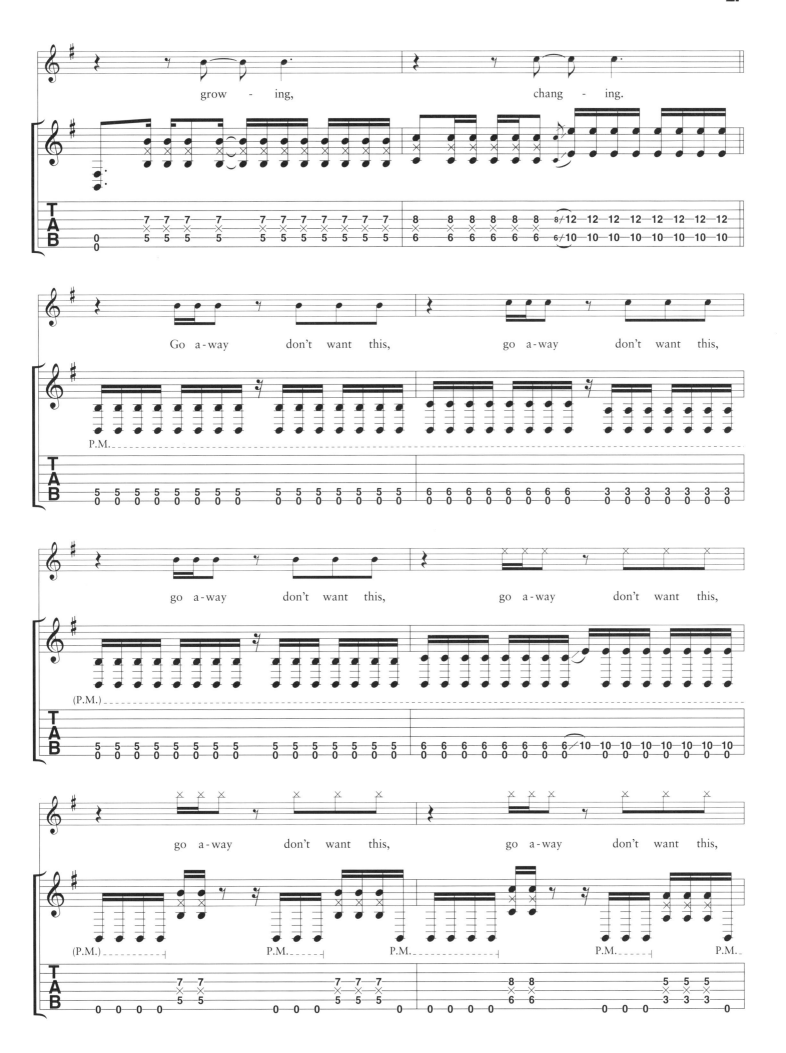

Crawling In The Dark

Words and Music by Douglas Robb and Daniel Estrin

All gtrs. w/Open E tuning:
E-B-E-G♯-B-E
⑥ = E   ③ = G♯
⑤ = B   ② = B
④ = E   ① = E

Moderate rock ♩ = 92

Intro:
N.C.

Gtr. 1 *(w/slight dist.)*

mf *w/delay*

P.M. throughout

Gtr. 1 tacet

E5 F♯5   E5 F♯5 D5   A/C♯ A5   E5

Gtr. 2 *(w/dist.)*

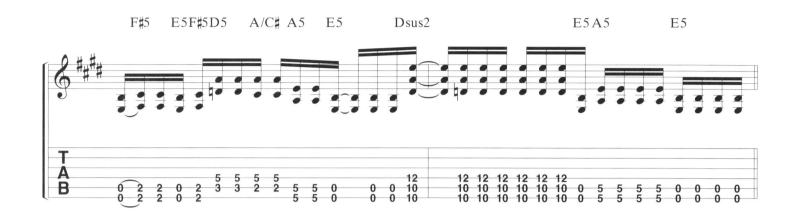

Verse:

1. I_____ will_ ded-i - cate_ and sac-ri - fice_ my_ ev - 'ry -
2. Help_ me_ car-ry on_ and show me it's_ o - kay_ to

thing for just a sec - ond's_ worth.__ I found my sto-ry's_ end - ing.
use my heart and not_ my_ eyes____ and nav - i - gate_ the_ dark - ness.

w/Riff A *(Gtr. 1)*
w/misc. feedback *(next 3 meas.)*
w/Riff B *(Gtr. 3) 2 times, 2nd time only*

And I_____ wish   I could   know_____   of the di - rec - tions   that_ I   take_
Will_____ the   end - ing   be_____   ev - er   com - ing   sud - den - ly?_

w/Fill 1 *(Gtr. 2) 1st time*
w/Rhy. Fill 1 *(Gtr. 2) 2nd time*

_____   and all the   choic - es   that_ I_____ make_____   won't end up   all_____ for   noth - ing.
_____   Will I   ev - er   get_ to_ see_____   the end - ing   to_____ my   sto - ry?

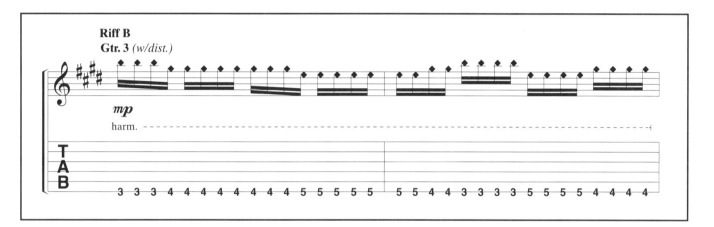

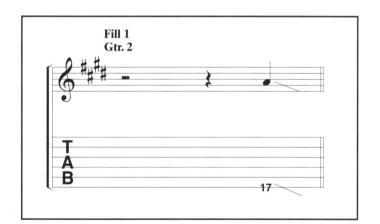

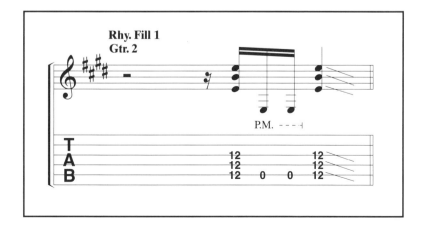

Chorus:
Gtr. 1 tacet
2nd time, Gtr. 3 tacet

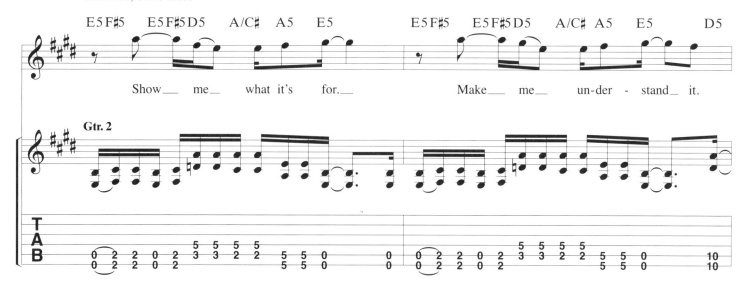

Show__ me__ what it's for.__ Make__ me__ un-der-stand__ it.

Double-time feel

end Double-time feel

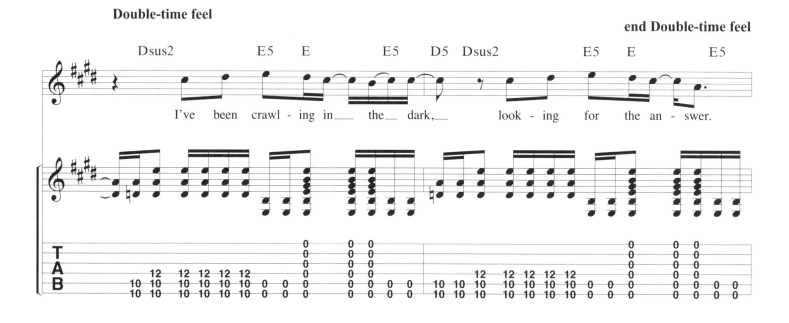

I've been crawl-ing in__ the__ dark,__ look-ing for the an - swer.

3rd time, Double-time feel

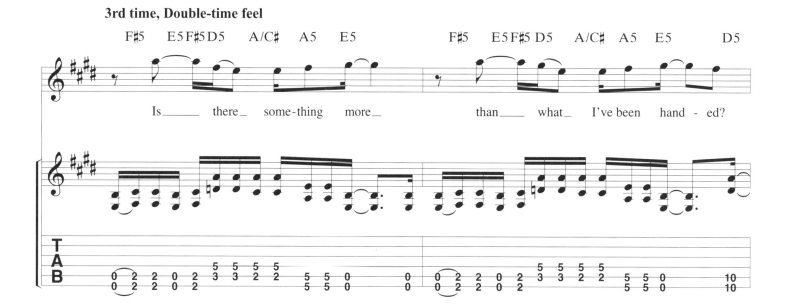

Is_____ there_ some-thing more__ than_____ what_ I've been hand - ed?

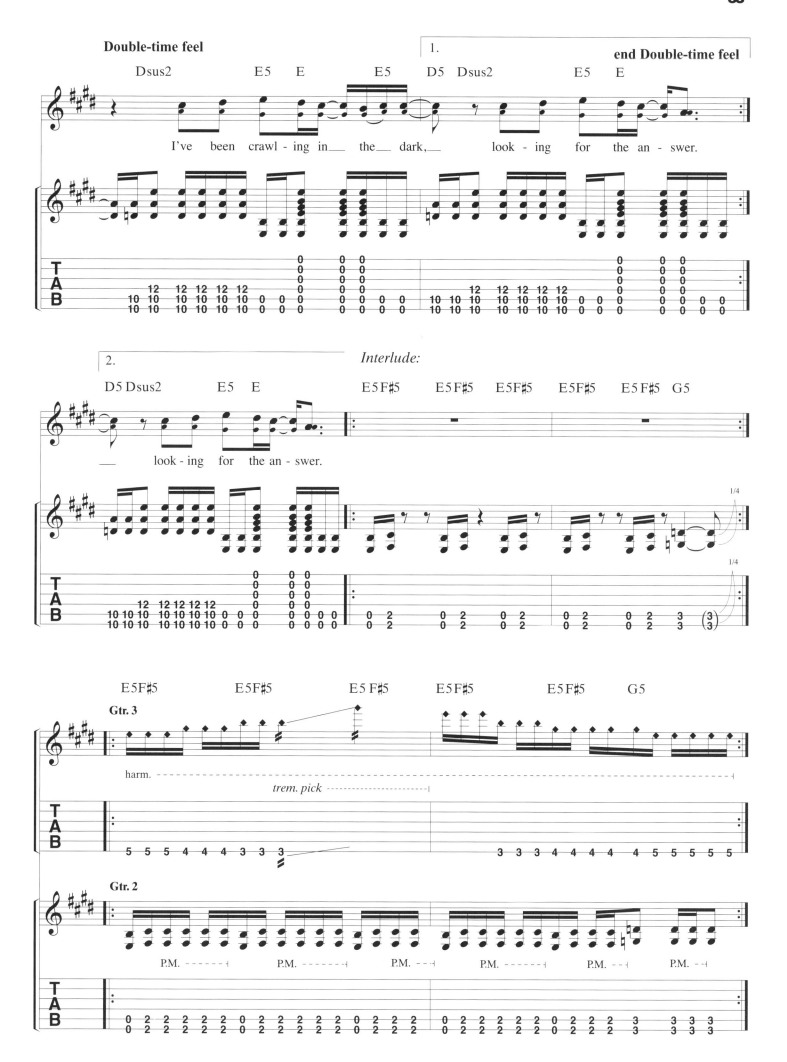

Bridge:
w/misc. Bkgd. Vcls.

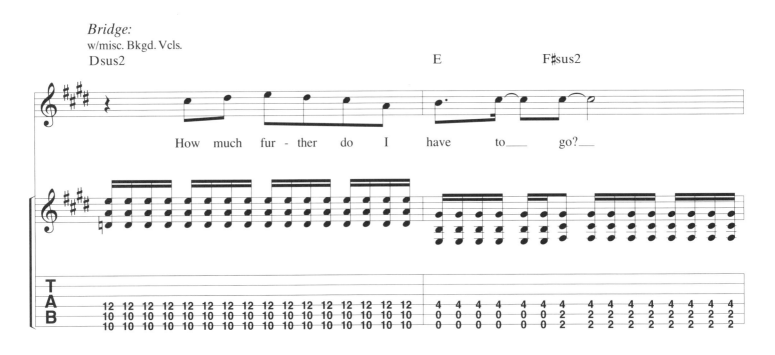

How much fur-ther do I have to___ go?___

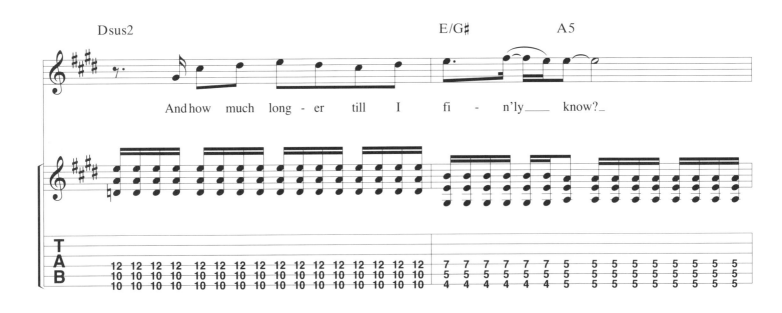

And how much long-er till I fi-n'ly___ know?___

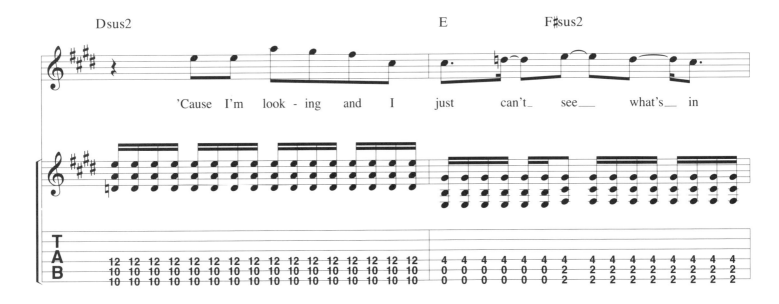

'Cause I'm look-ing and I just can't___ see___ what's___ in

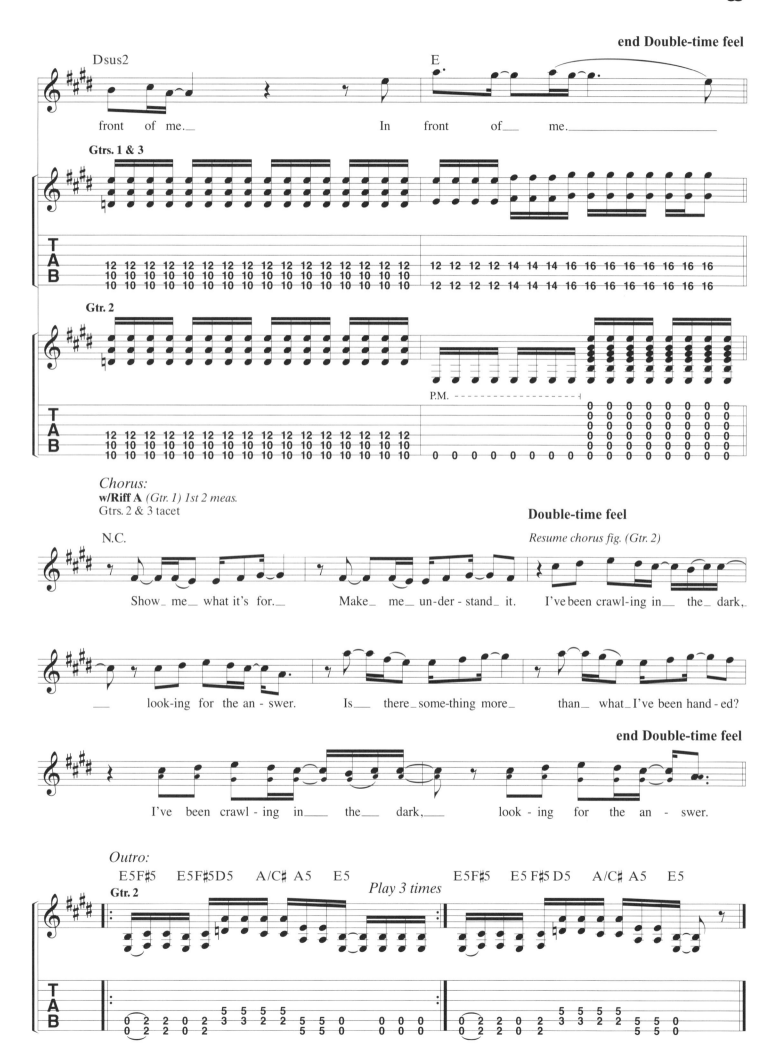

Cochise

Words and Music by Christopher Cornell, Timothy Commerford, Tom Morello and Brad Wilkes

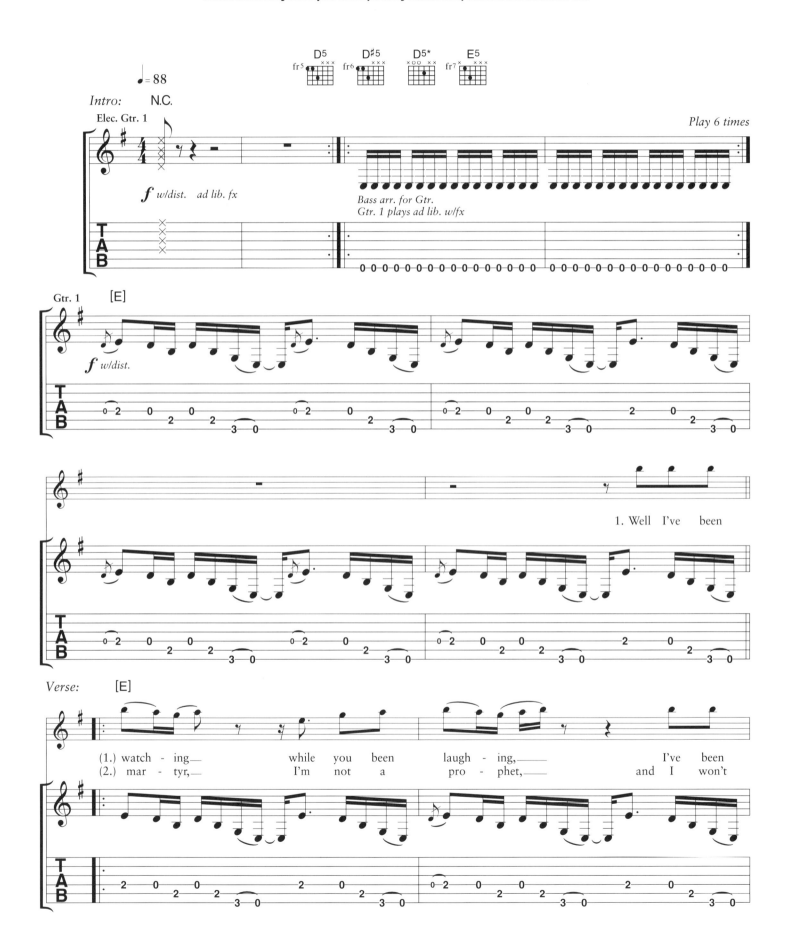

Demon Speeding

Words and Music by Rob Zombie and Scott Humphrey

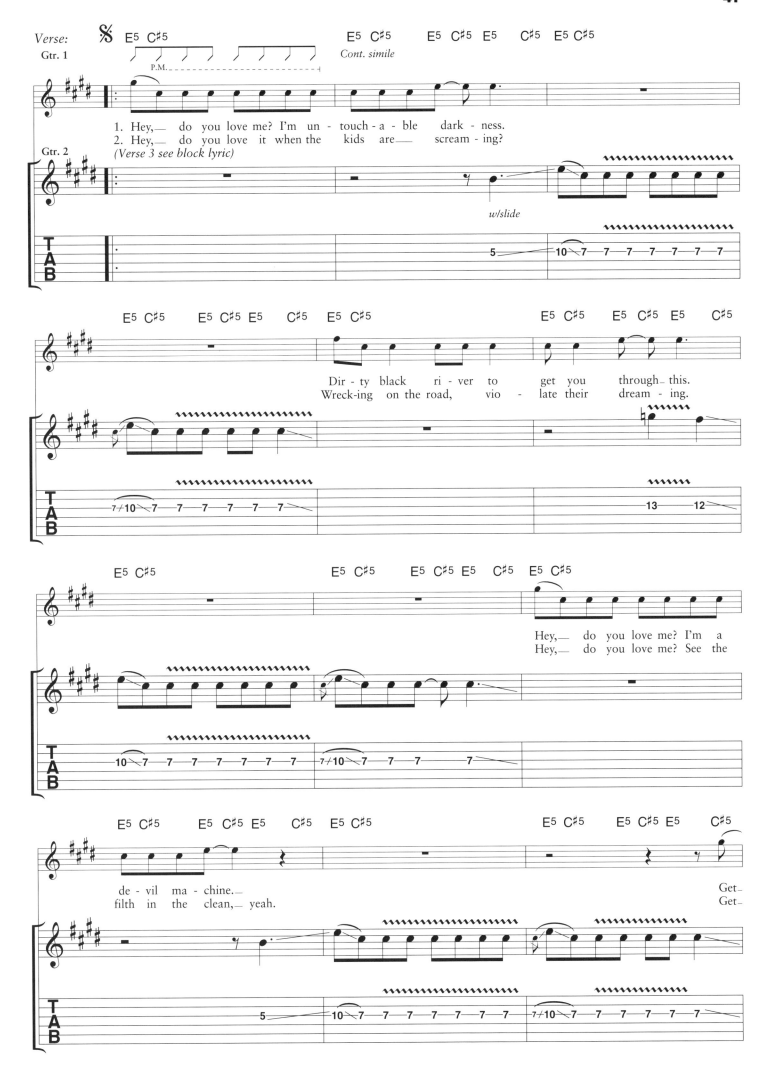

Verse 3:
Hey, do you love me elevating the madness?
A super death arising to get you through this
Hey, do you love me like a beautiful fiend, yeah.
Get into my world all American dream.

Fade

Words and Music by Michael Mushok, Aaron Lewis, John April and Jonathan Wysocki

All gtrs. tune to:
⑥ = A♭   ③ = D♭
⑤ = E♭   ② = G♭
④ = A♭   ① = B♭

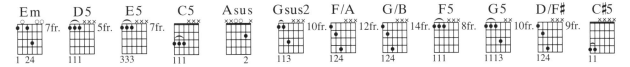

Moderately ♩ = 108

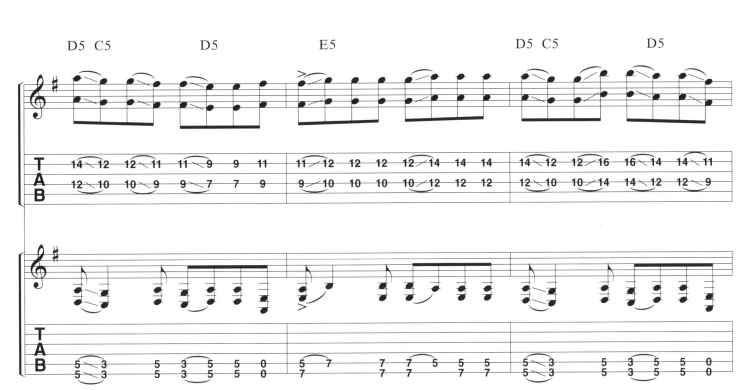

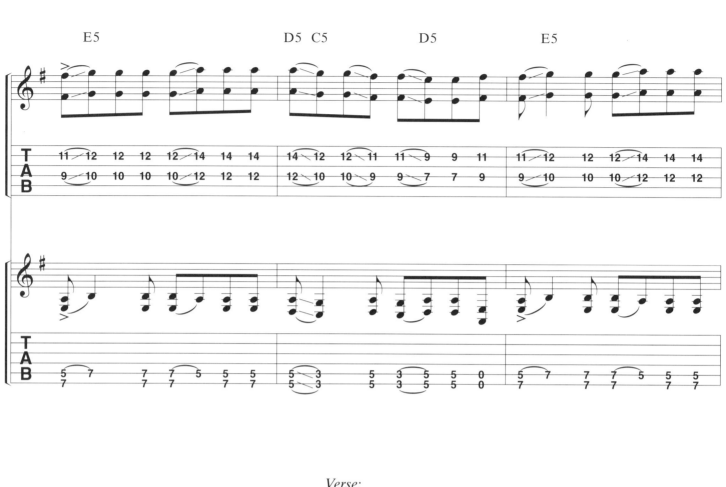

Verse:

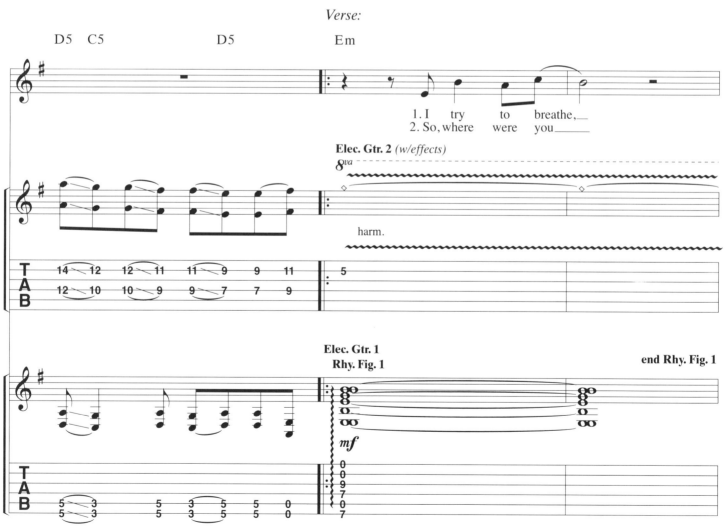

w/**Rhy. Fig. 1** *(Elec. Gtr. 1) 3 times, simile*

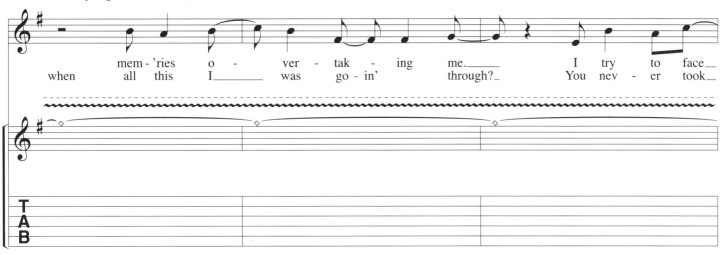

when mem - 'ries o - ver - tak - ing me._____ I try to face__
all this I_____ was go - in' through?_ You nev - er took__

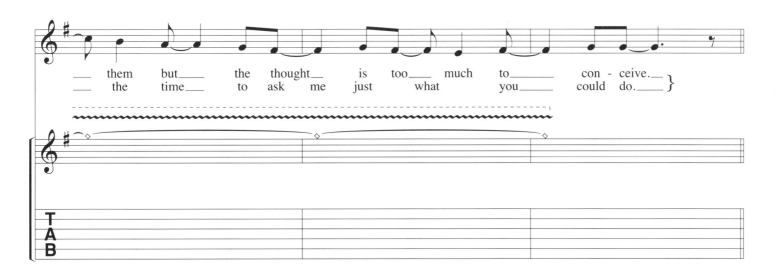

___ them but____ the thought__ is too___ much to_____ con - ceive._
___ the time___ to ask me just what you_____ could do._

Pre-chorus:

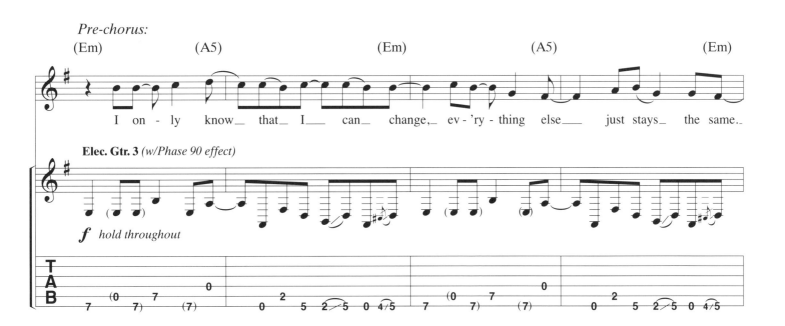

I on - ly know_ that_ I__ can change, ev - 'ry - thing else___ just stays_ the same._

Elec. Gtr. 3 *(w/Phase 90 effect)*

f *hold throughout*

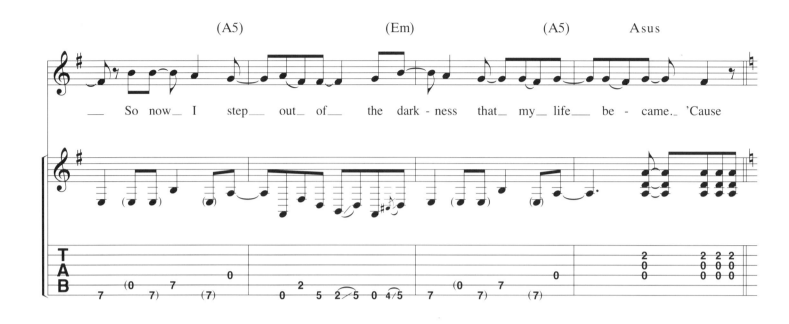

(A5) (Em) (A5) Asus

So now__ I step__ out__ of__ the dark-ness that__ my life__ be-came.__ 'Cause

𝄋 *Chorus:*

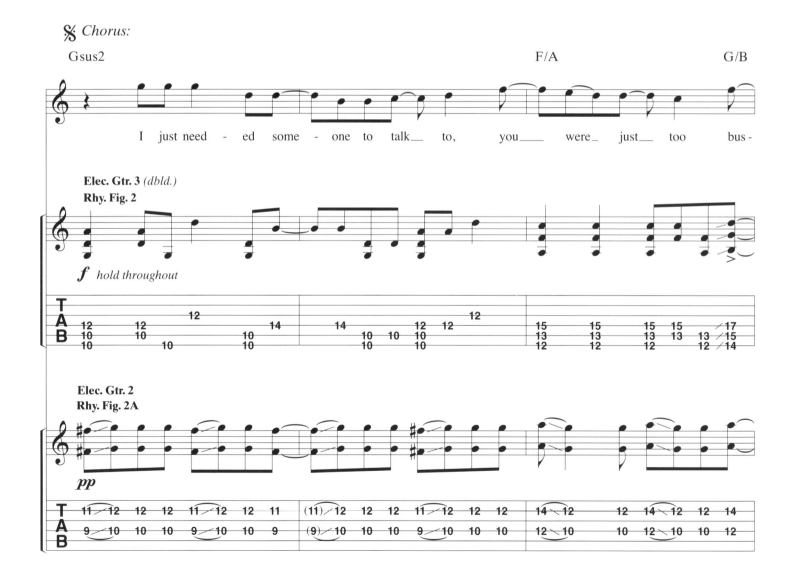

Gsus2 F/A G/B

I just need-ed some-one to talk__ to, you__ were__ just__ too bus-

Elec. Gtr. 3 *(dbld.)*
Rhy. Fig. 2

f *hold throughout*

Elec. Gtr. 2
Rhy. Fig. 2A

pp

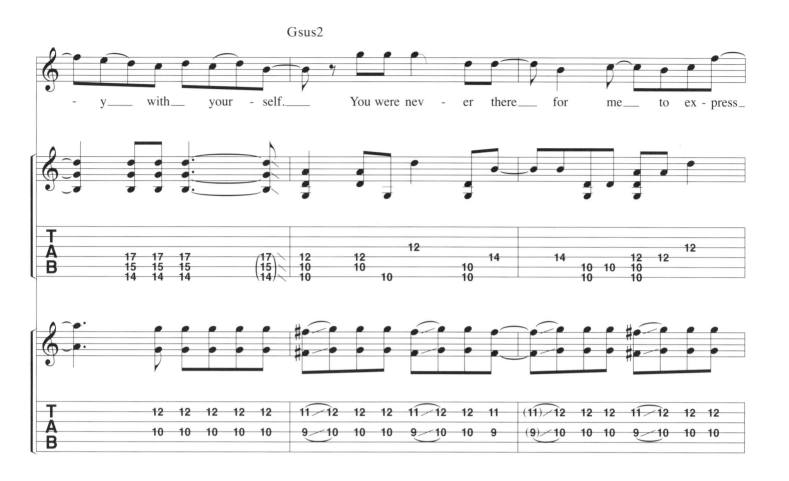

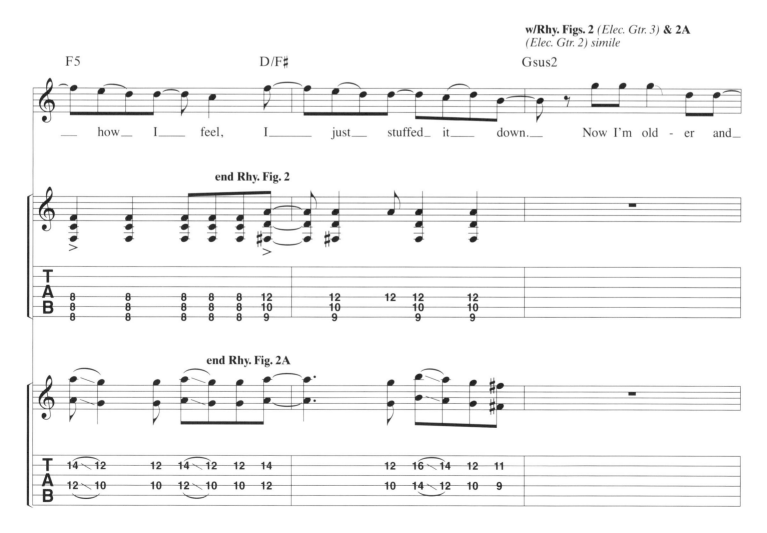

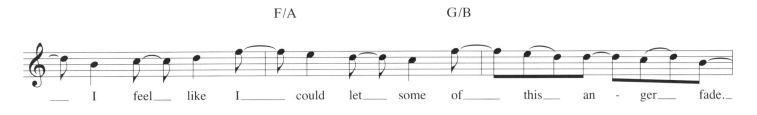

I feel__ like I__ could let__ some of__ this__ an - ger__ fade.__

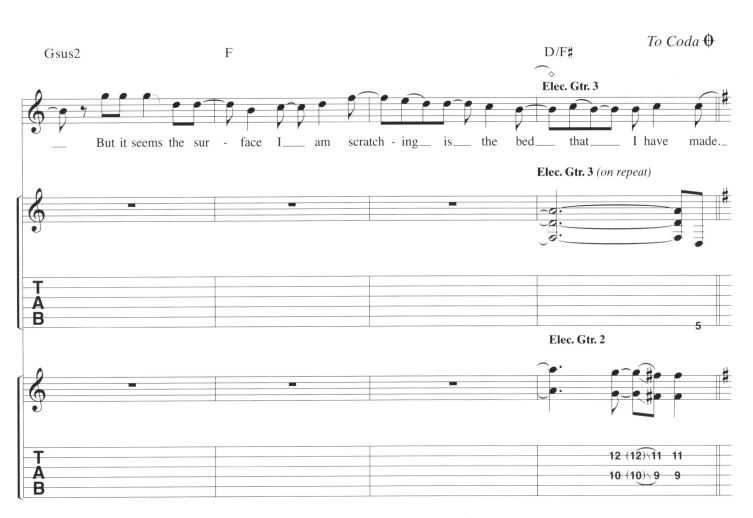

But it seems the sur - face I__ am scratch - ing__ is__ the bed__ that__ I have made.__

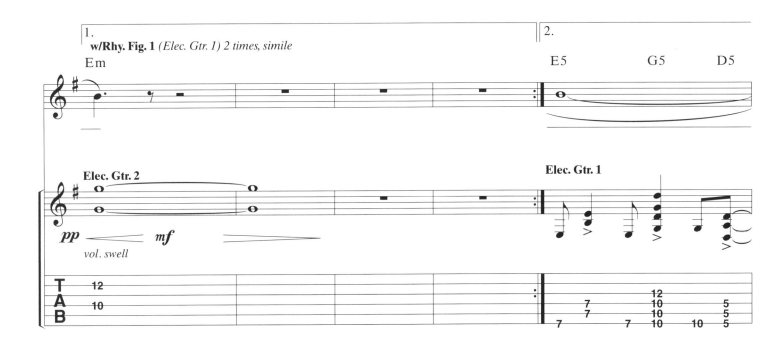

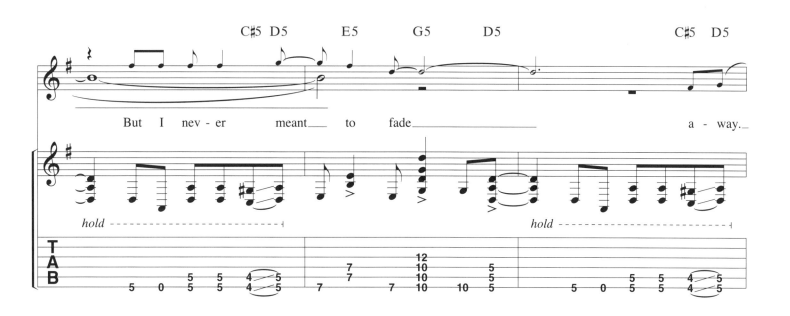

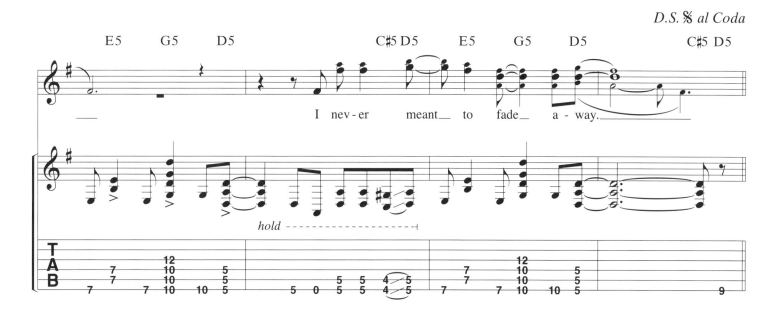

Outro:

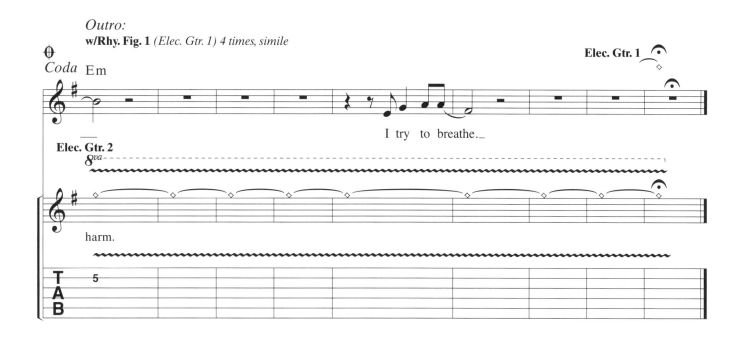

Drift And Die

Words and Music by Wesley Scantlin and Jimmy Allen

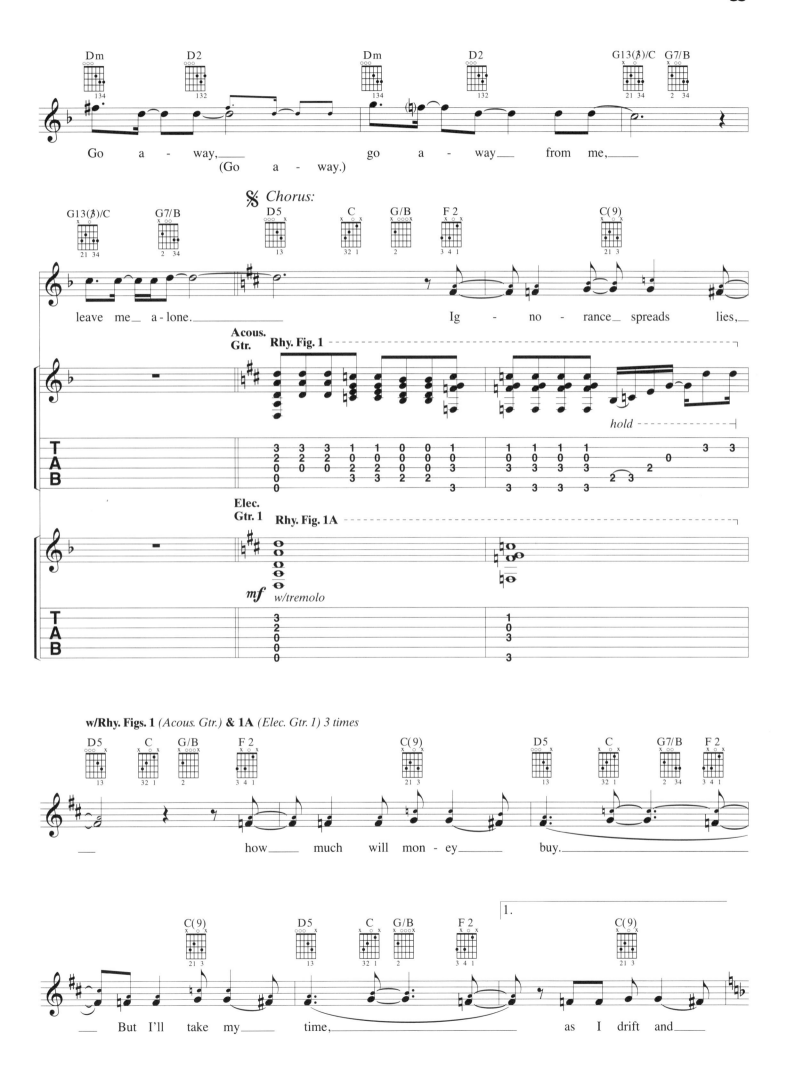

As I drift____ and die._____

As I drift____ and die._____

Drowning

Words and Music by Bret Mazur, Seth Binzer, Doug Miller, Anthony Vali and Craig Tyler

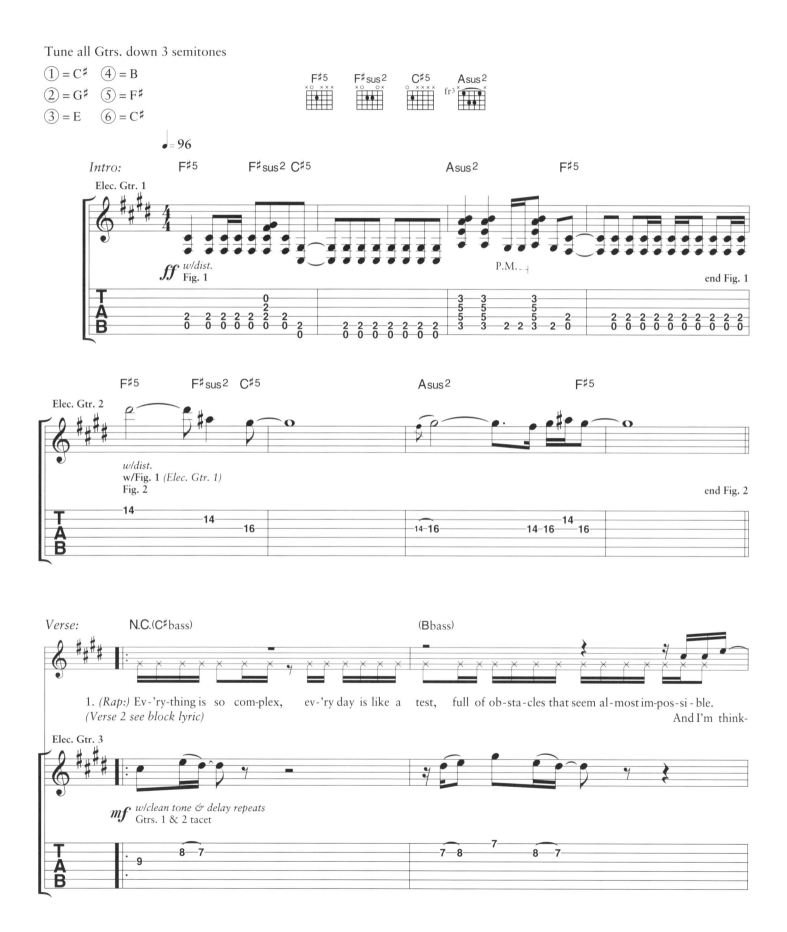

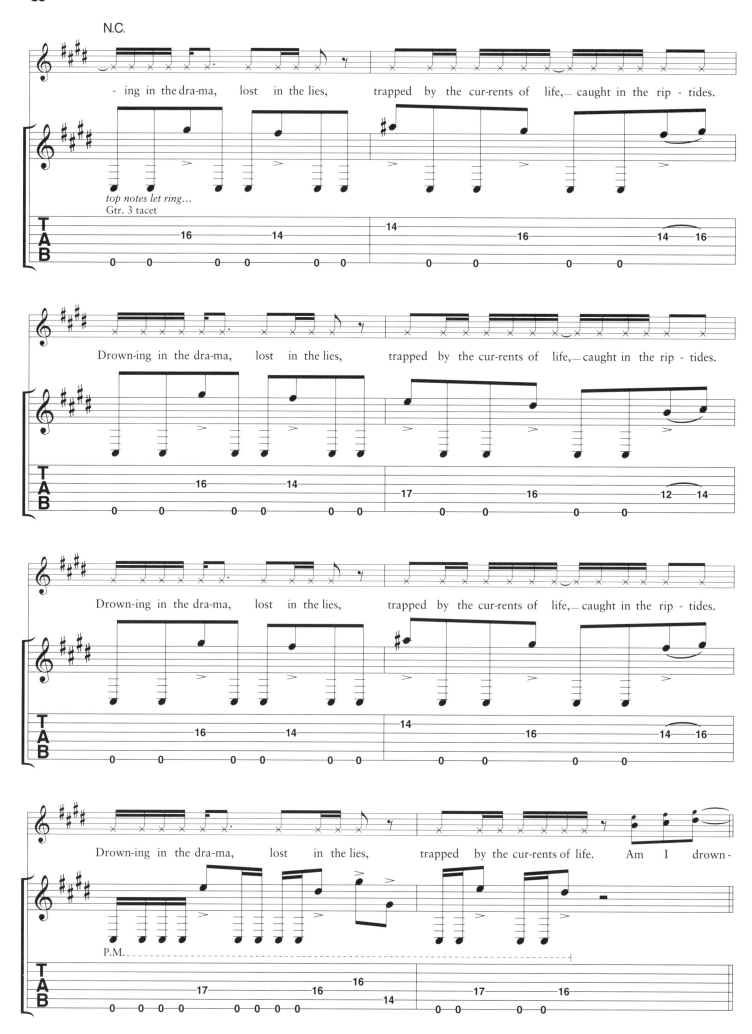

Verse 2:
There was a time
That I questioned if I'd ever be alright
Running, getting high, staying trapped by sleepless nights.

And I'm thinking, just another breath, not a minute left
I feel there's something missing.

I'm running from myself and all the things I don't like
Living every night like it's the last night.

And I'm thinking, just another prayer, not a second left
I need to stop resisting.

Fuck The Voodooman

Words and Music by Frank Regan, John Loughlin, Anthony Loughlin, Gareth Smith, Darren Smith and Gordon Morison

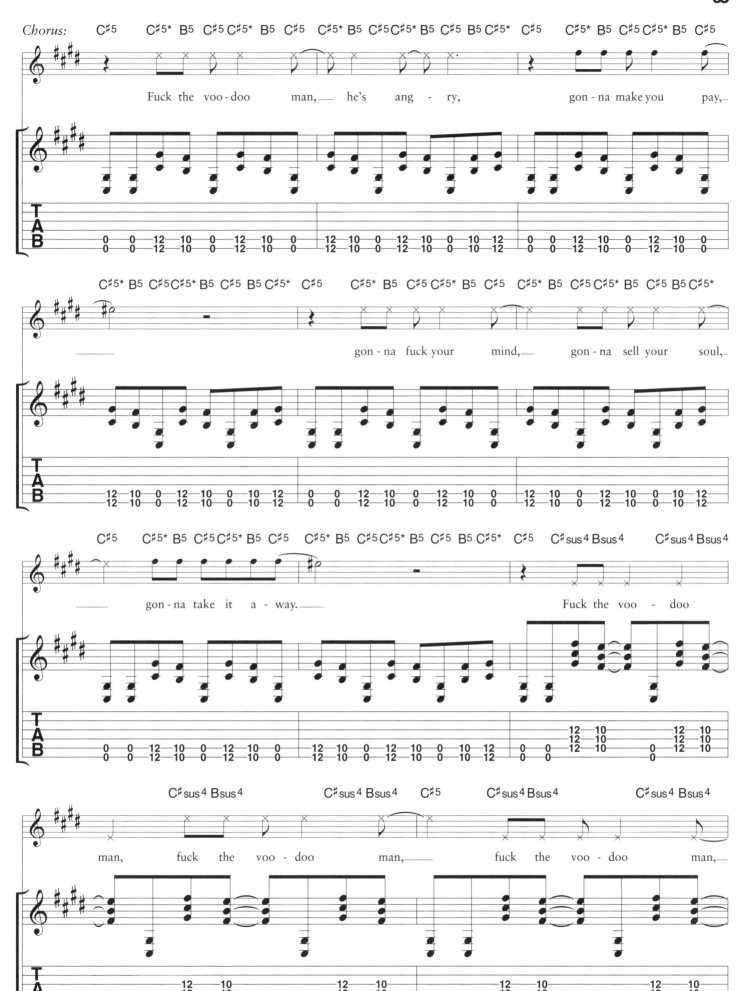

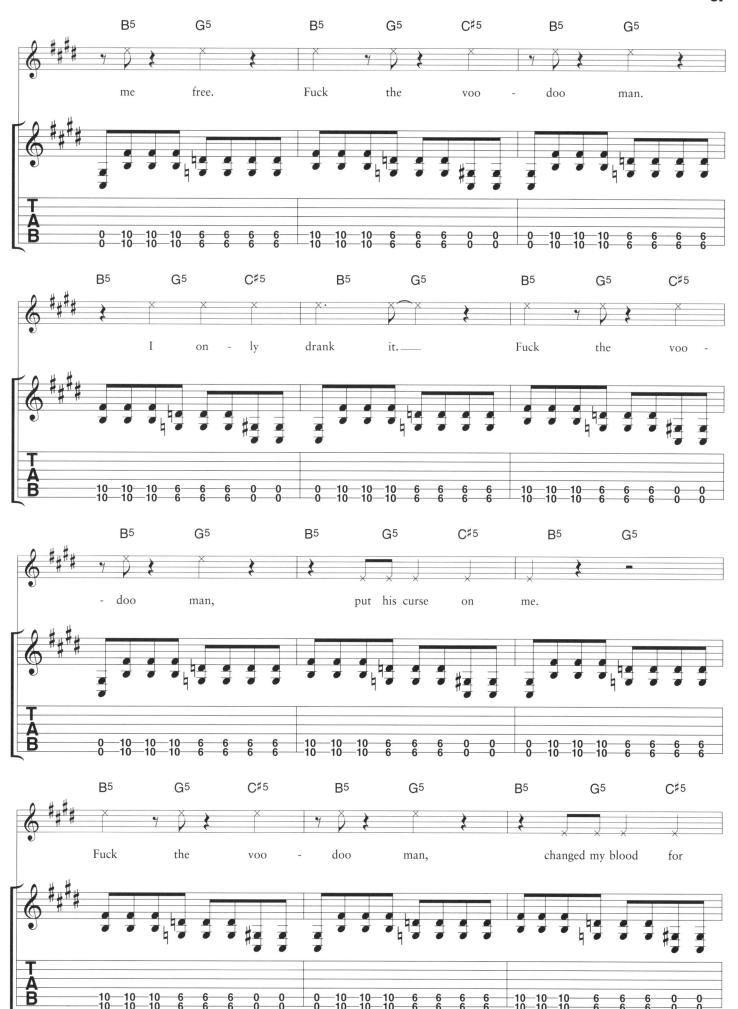

Gets Me Through

Words and Music by Ozzy Osbourne and Tim Palmer

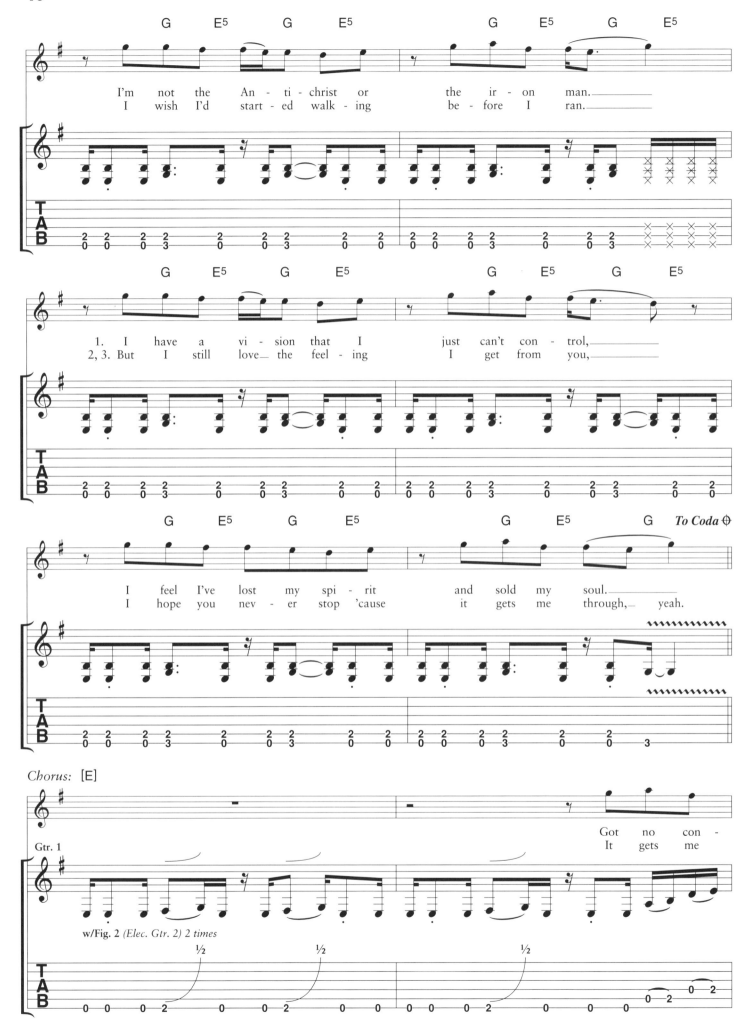

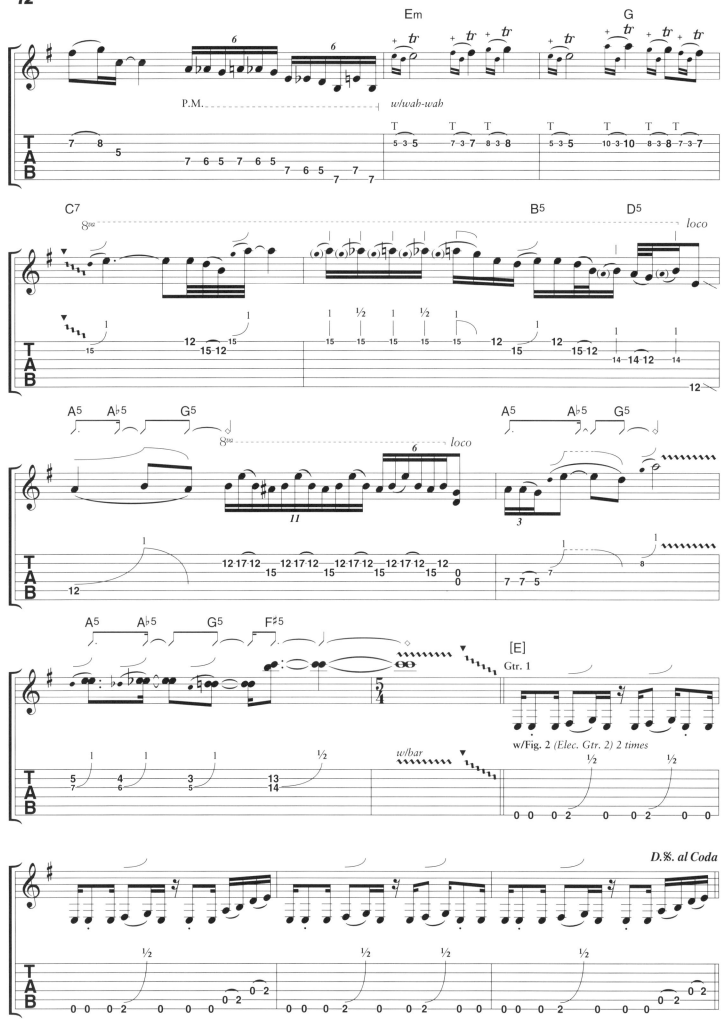

Get Up Again

Words and Music by Chris Voltz, Ryan Juhrs, Chris Ballinger, Jason Daunt and Lance Amy

Tune all Gtrs.
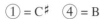
① = C♯   ④ = B
② = G♯   ⑤ = F♯
③ = E   ⑥ = B

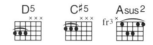

♩ = 95

Intro: N.C.
Elec. Gtr. 1

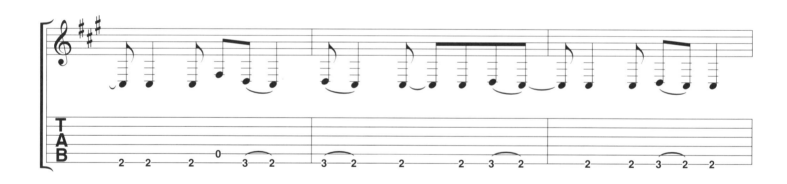

Key signature denotes C♯ phrygian

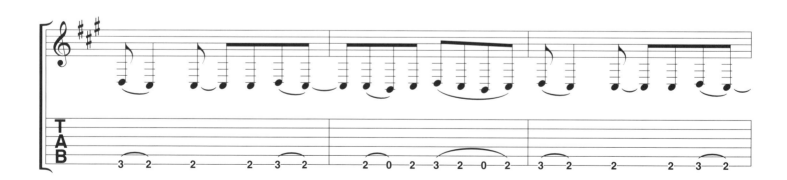

Here we go a-gain.

D5 C#5   D5 C#5   D5 C#5   D5 C#5   D5 C#5

Gtrs. 1 & 2

ff

1.   N.C.   2.   N.C.

1. A ve-ry tem-p'ra-men-tal

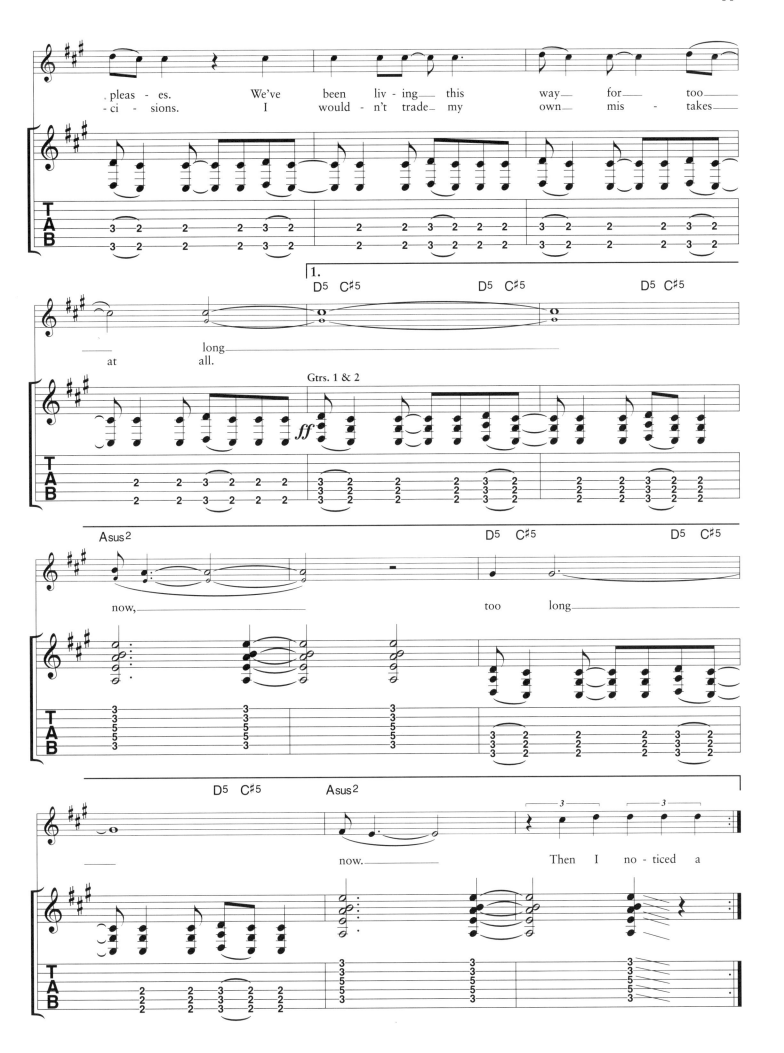

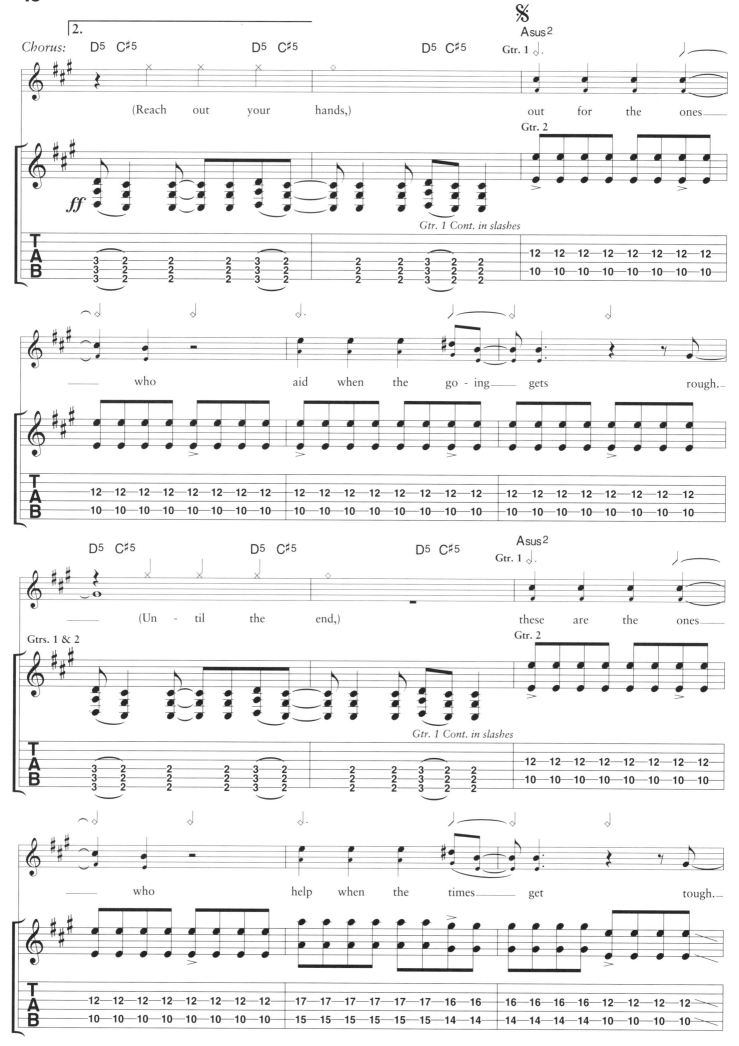

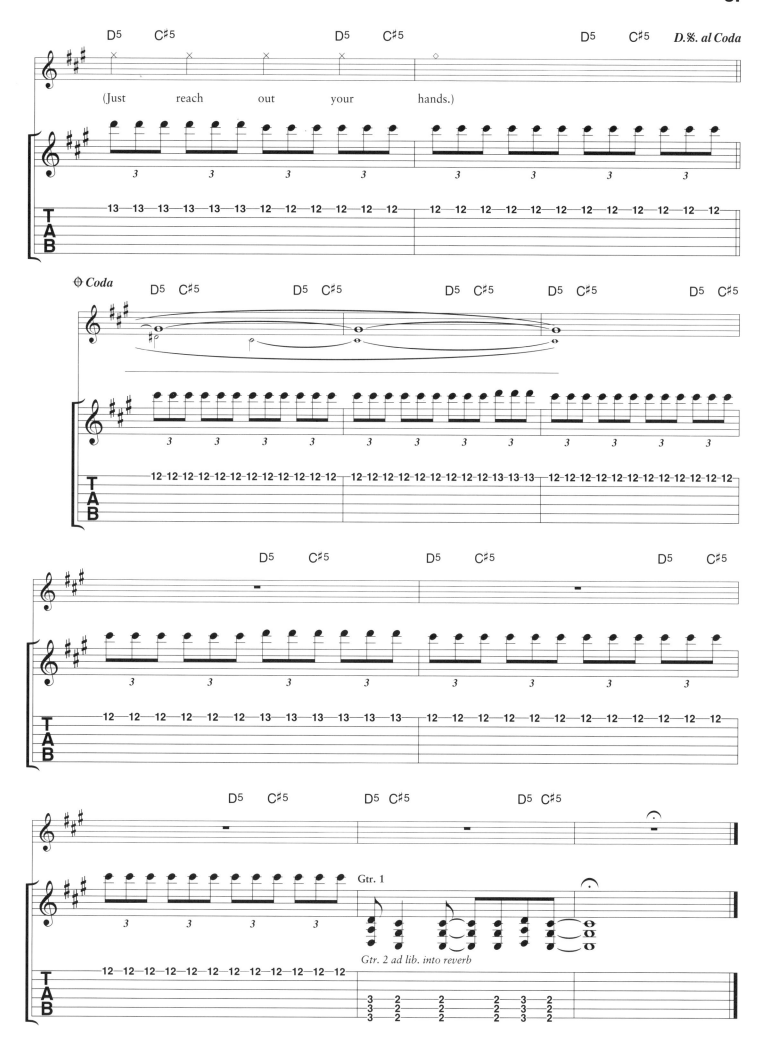

(Just reach out your hands.)

⊕ *Coda*

Gtr. 1

Gtr. 2 ad lib. into reverb

God Save Us

Words and Music by Christian Machado, Dave Chavarri and Marc Rizzo

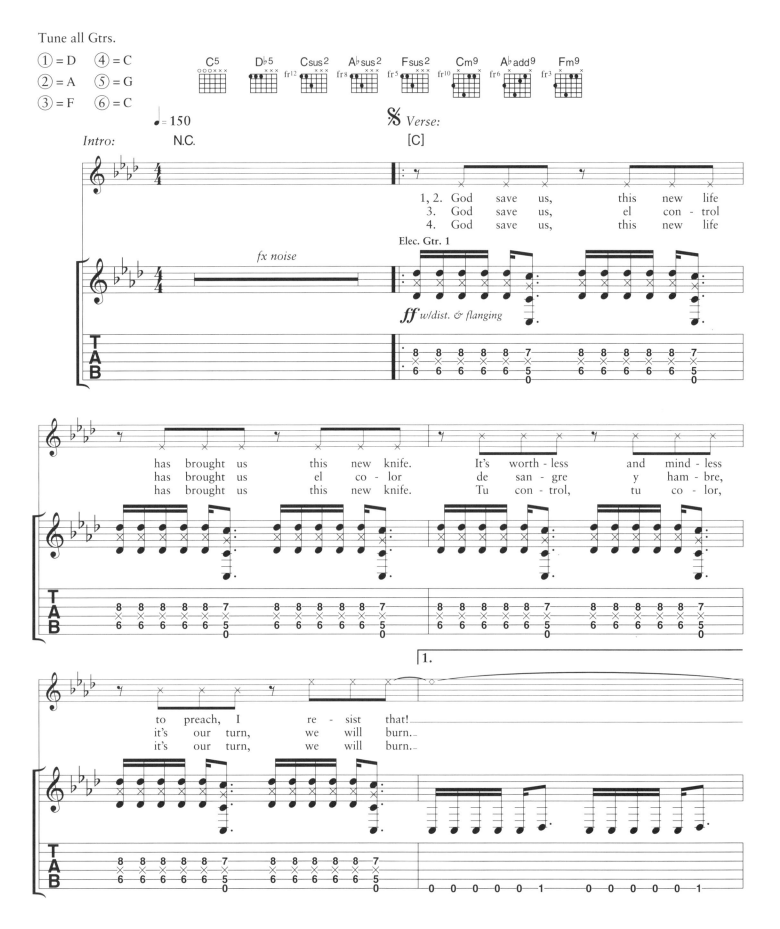

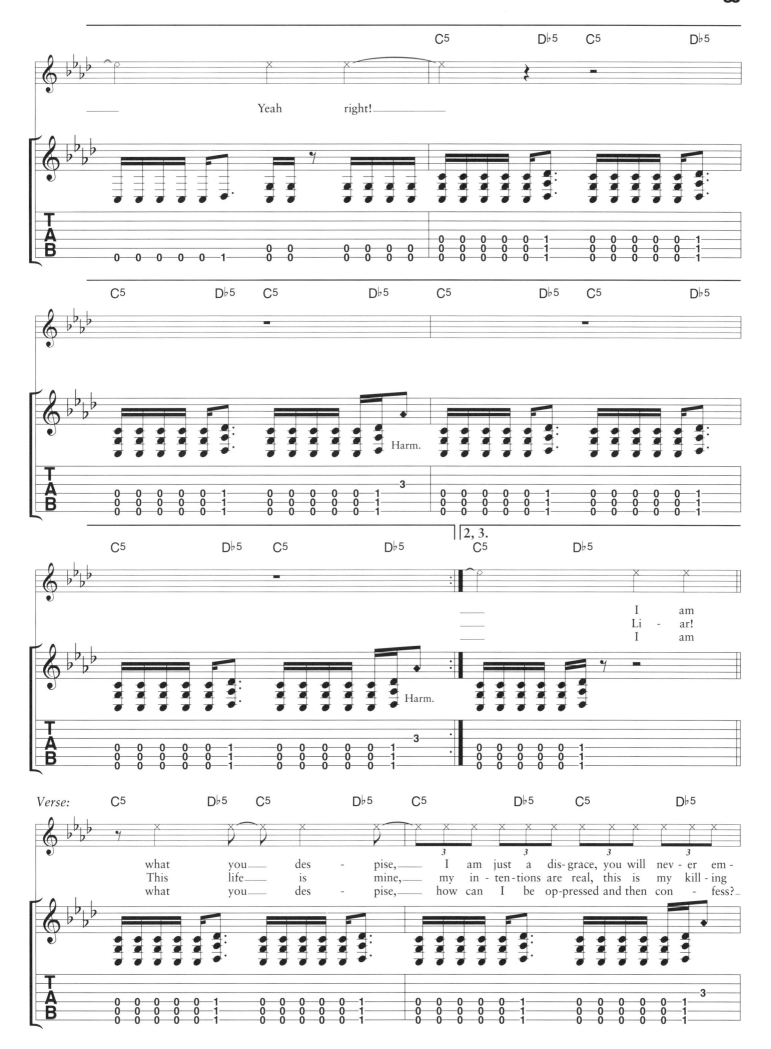

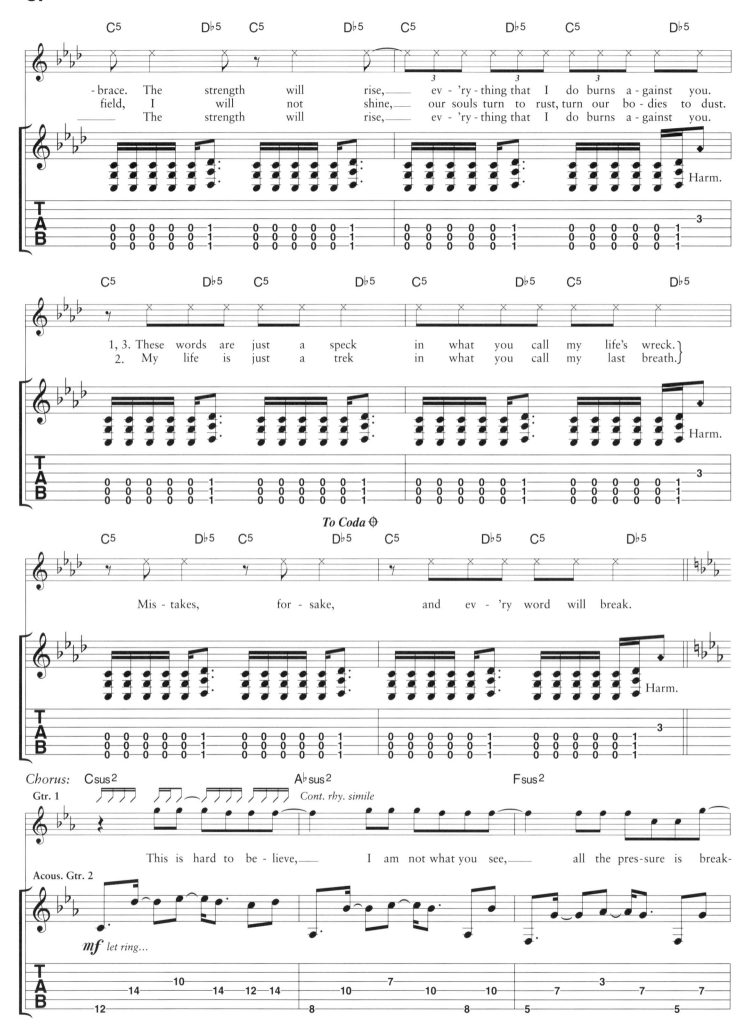

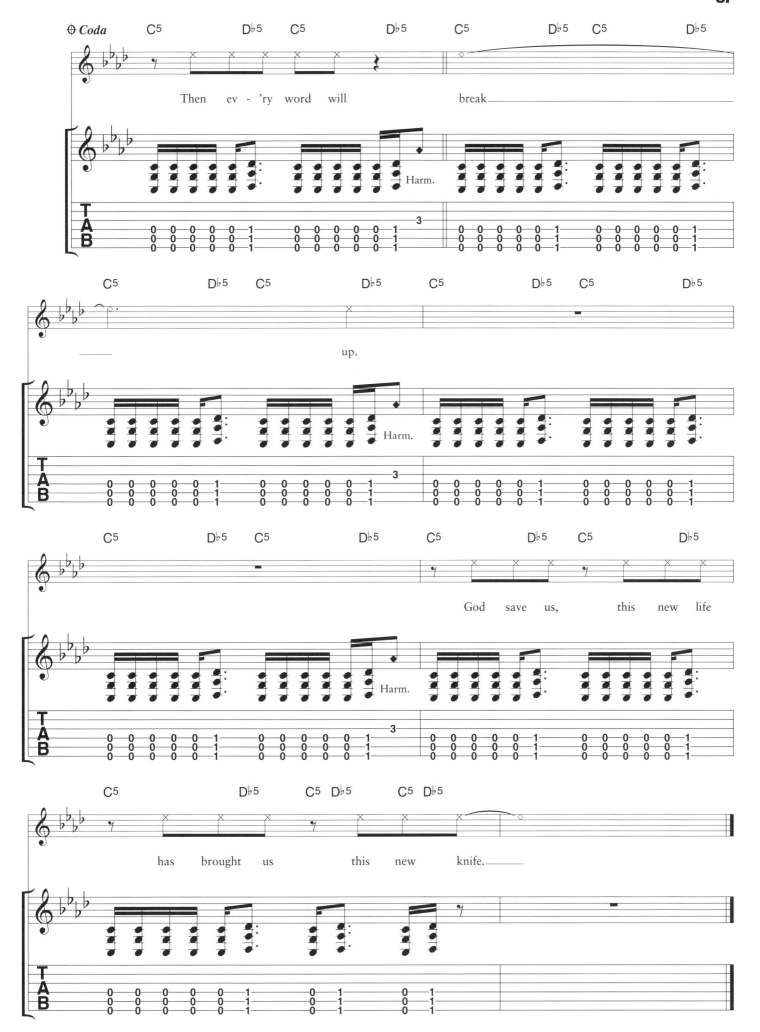

The Hate Song

Words and Music by Frank Regan, John Loughlin, Anthony Loughlin, Gareth Smith, Darren Smith and Gordon Morison

My Plague

Words and Music by James Root, Craig Jones, Michael Crahan, Paul Gray, Nathan Jordison, Corey Taylor, Christopher Fehn, Mickael Thompson and Sidney Wilson

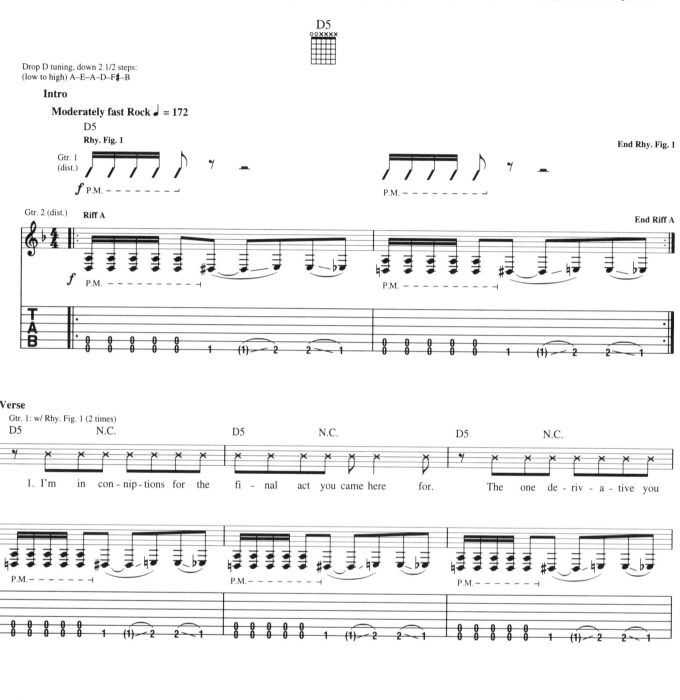

Drop D tuning, down 2 1/2 steps:
(low to high) A–E–A–D–F#–B

Intro

Moderately fast Rock ♩ = 172

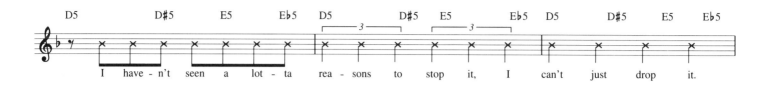

I have-n't seen a lot-ta rea-sons to stop it, I can't just drop it.

D.S. al Coda 1
End half-time feel

I'm just a bas-tard but at least I ad - mit it. At least I ad - mit it! _____

Gtrs. 1 & 2

P.M.

⊕ Coda 1
Interlude

N.C.

self!

Riff B1
Gtr. 2
End Riff B1

P.M.

Gtr. 1 Riff B
End Riff B

P.M.

Gtrs. 1 & 2: w/ Riffs B & B1

Yeah! _____

Nightmare

Words and Music by Cliff Rigano, Scott Thompson and Philip Acuri III

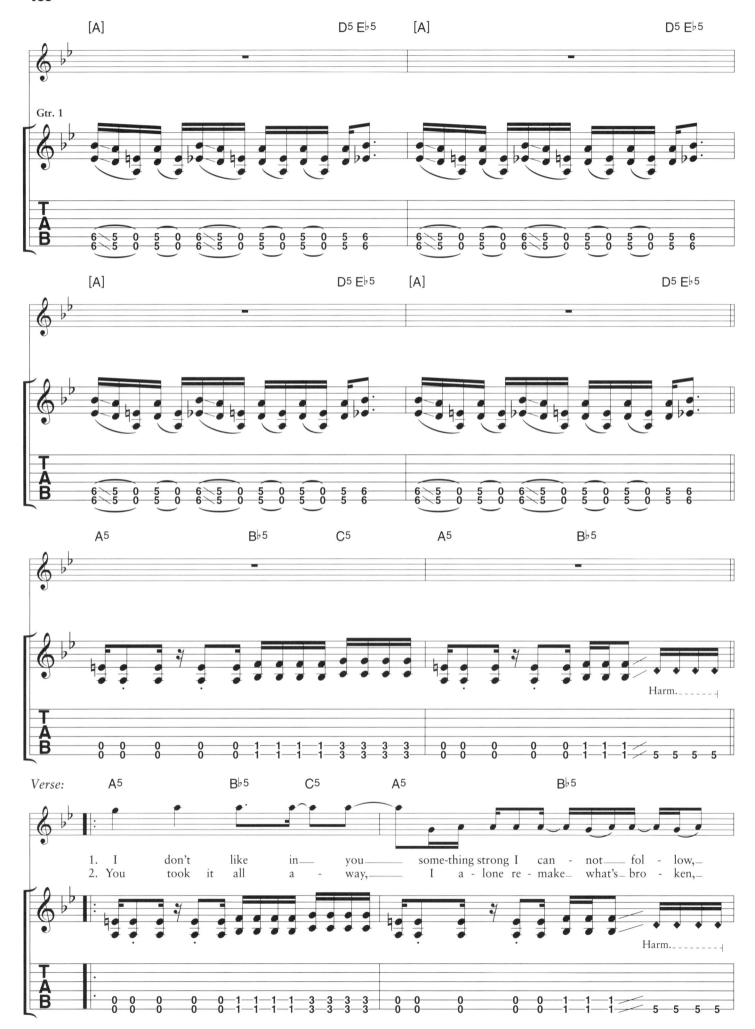

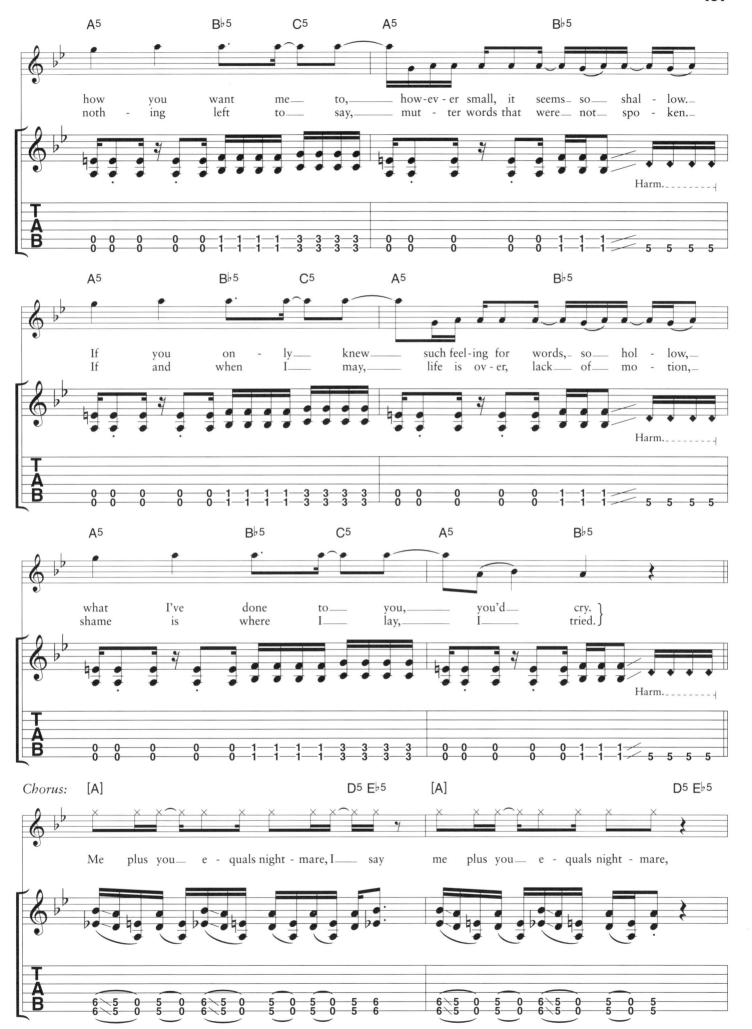

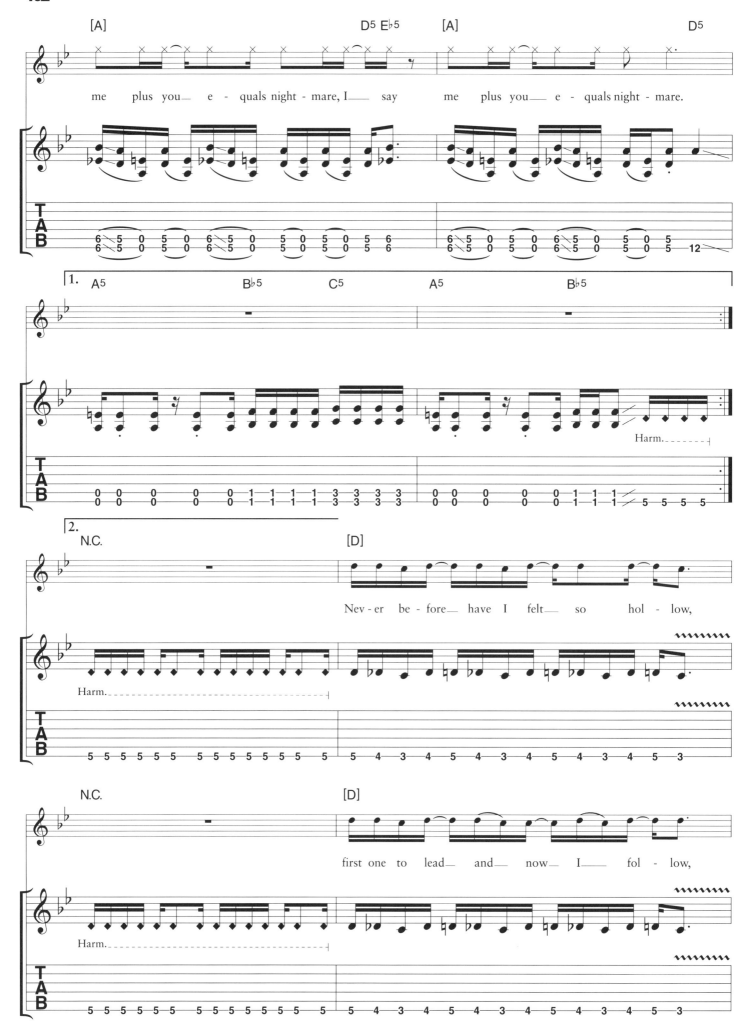

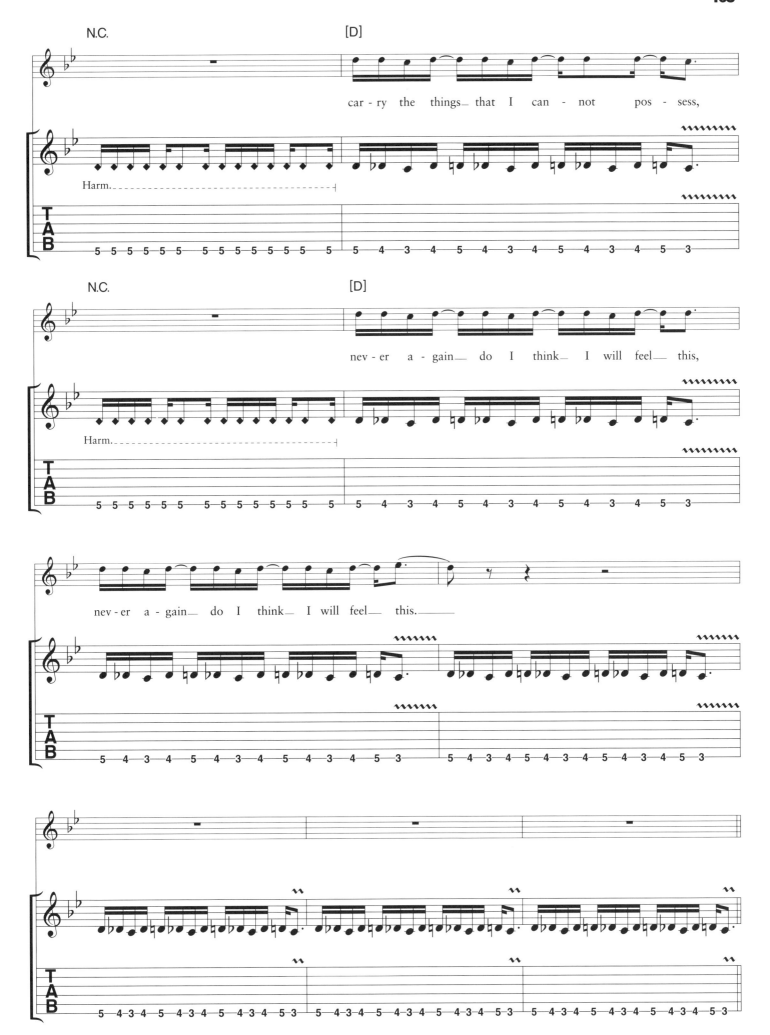

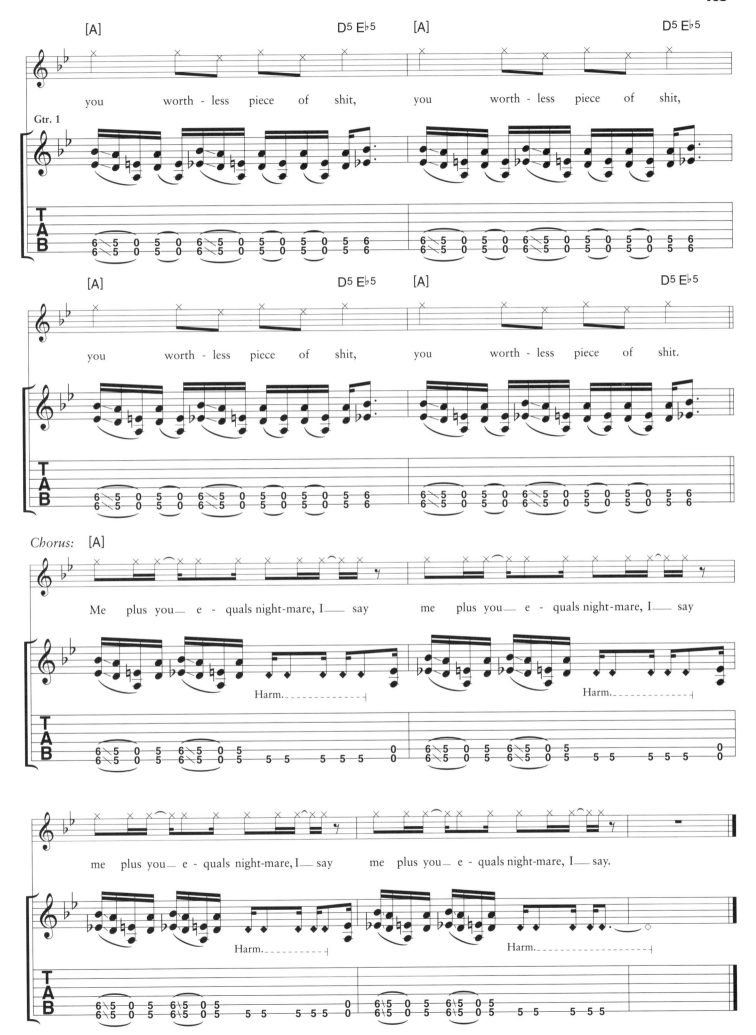

Nobodies

Words and Music by Brian Warner and John Lowery

*Glissando tremolo

People=Shit

Words and Music by James Root, Craig Jones, Michael Crahan, Paul Gray, Nathan Jordison, Corey Taylor, Christopher Fehn, Mickael Thompson and Sidney Wilson

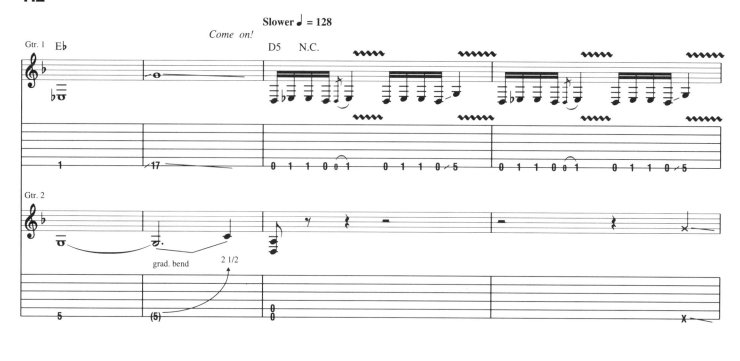

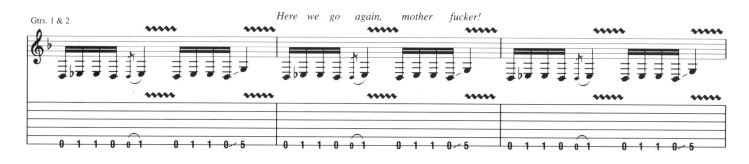

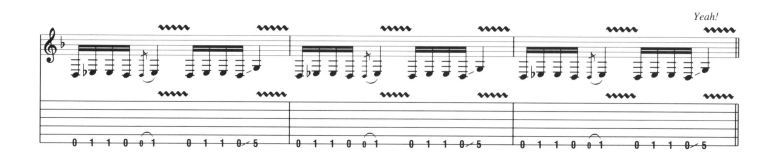

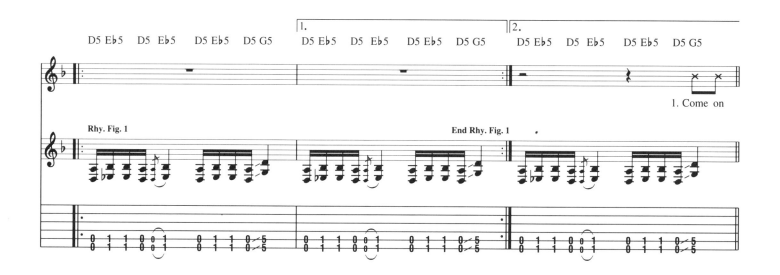

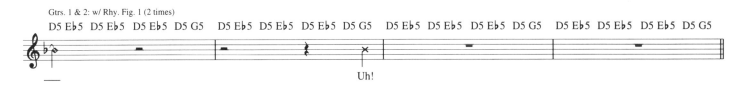

Bridge

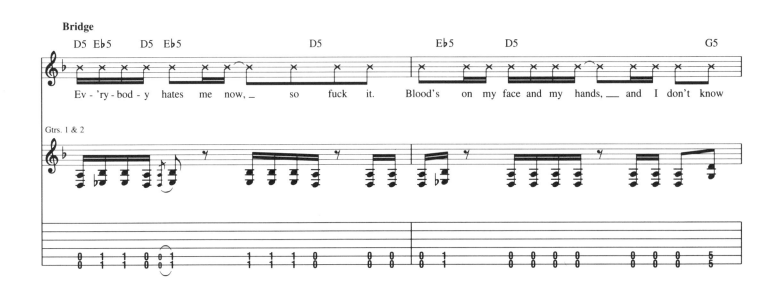

Ev - 'ry - bod - y hates me now, _ so fuck it. Blood's on my face and my hands, _ and I don't know

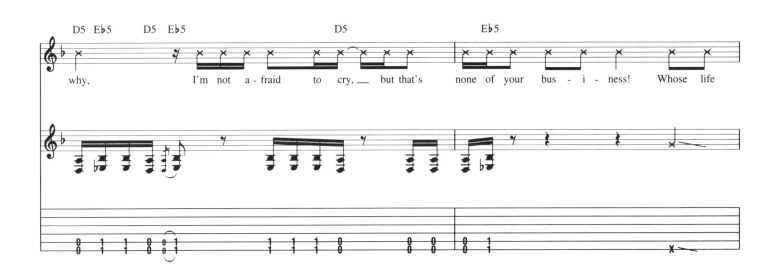

why, I'm not a - fraid to cry, _ but that's none of your bus - i - ness! Whose life

is it? Get it? See it? Feel it? Eat it? Spin it a - round _ so I can spit in its

face. I wan - na leave with - out _ a trace, cuz I don't wan - na die in this _ place! _

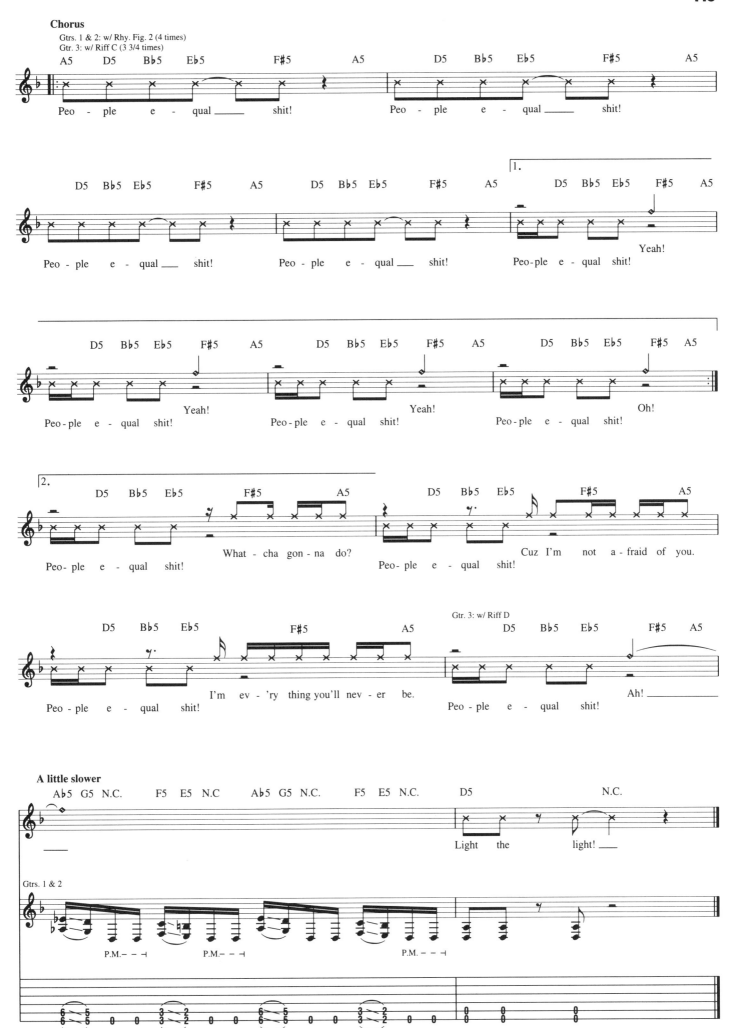

Oracle

Words and Music by Morgan Lander and Mercedes Lander

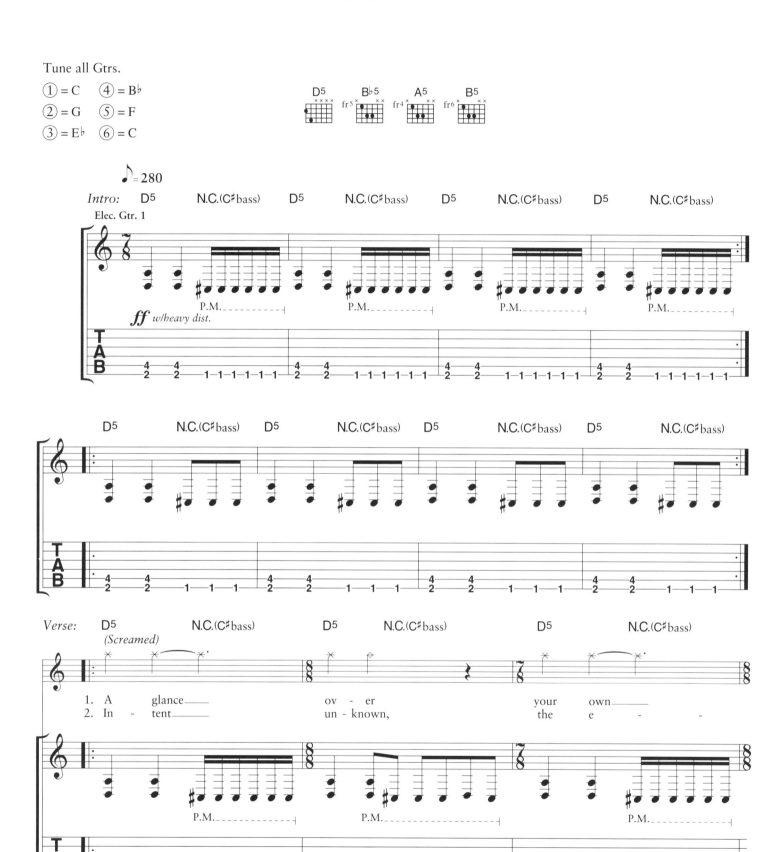

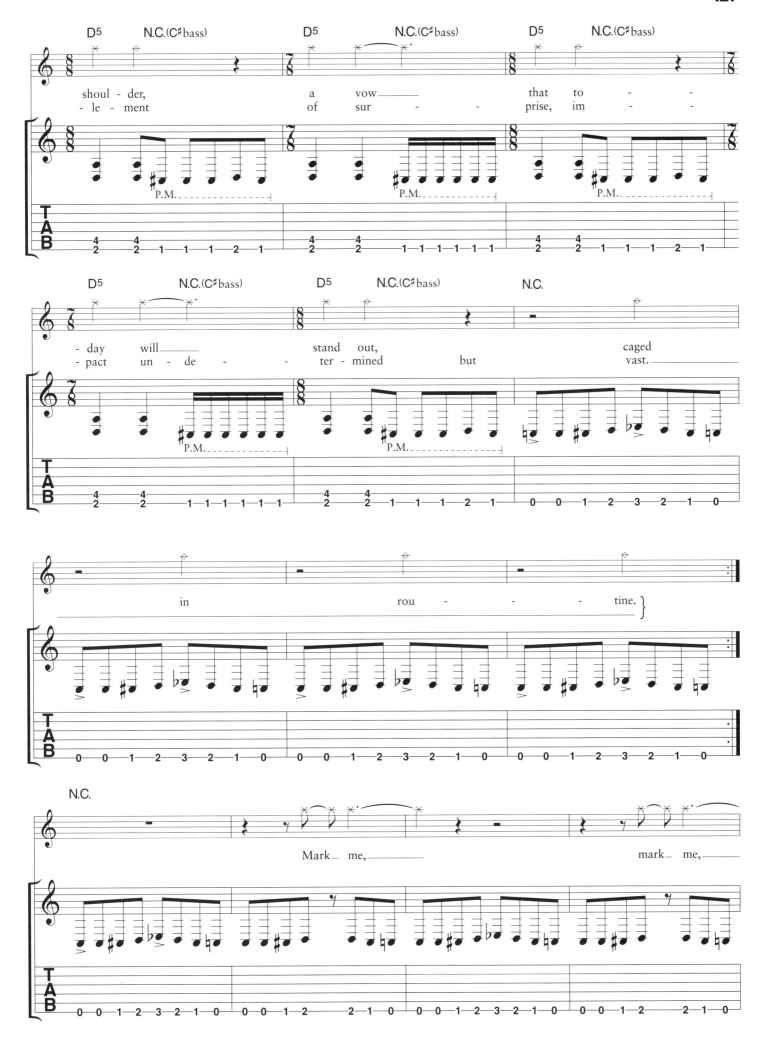

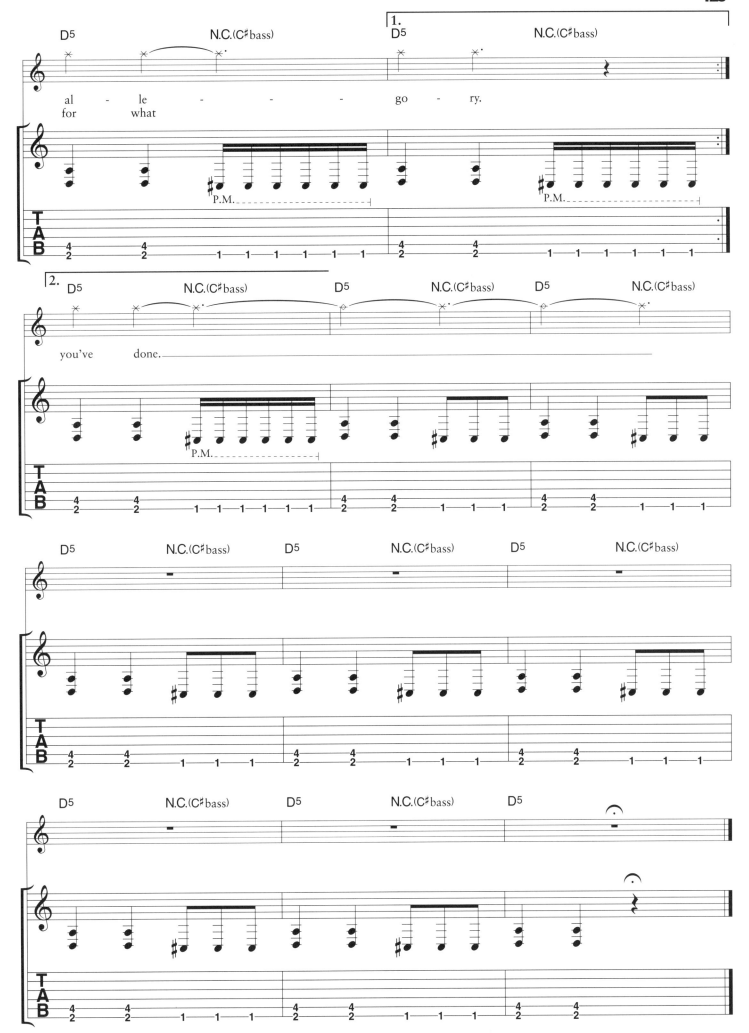

Perversions Of Pain

Words and Music by Jeff Hannemann and Kerry King

Instrumental: N.C.

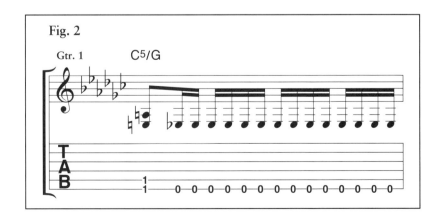

Lyrics: your sens - es un - der siege,____ in - gest the vir - tues I feed.____

D.𝄋. al Coda

⊕ *Coda*

Fig. 4

*Start at top of neck and slide down with dampened left hand

Gtrs. 1 & 2

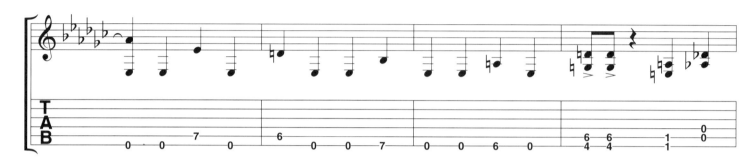

w/Fig. 5 (Elec. Gtr. 1)

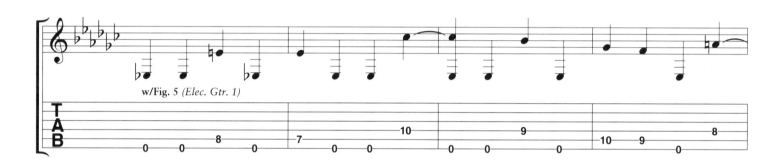

Gtrs. 1 & 2

G5*   Fb5

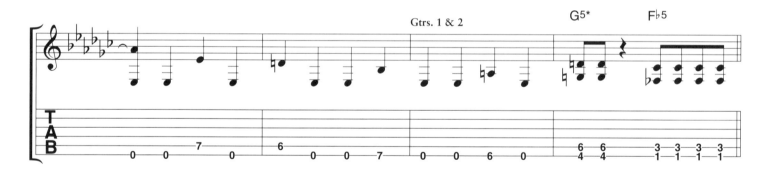

Fig. 5

Gtr. 1   N.C.

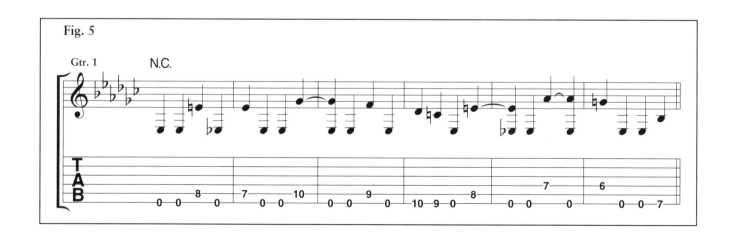

Verse 3:
A higher level of pain
Is racing through my veins
There's nothing more intense
Than mental misery that I dispense.
So follow right along
Observe a fresh new dawn
Of super sensation
My realm of torture stimulation.

Remember

Words and Music by Mike Wengren, Dan Donegan, David Draiman and Steve Kmak

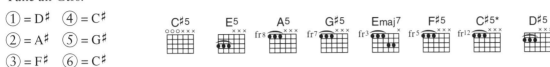

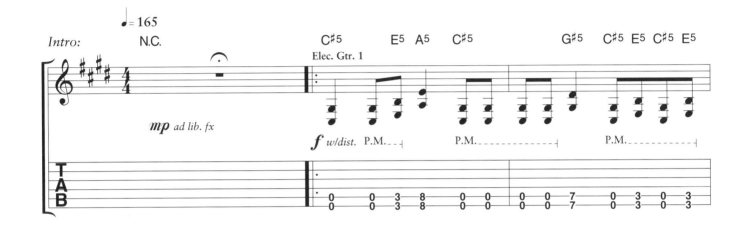

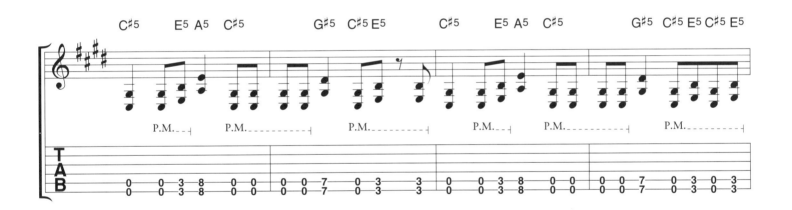

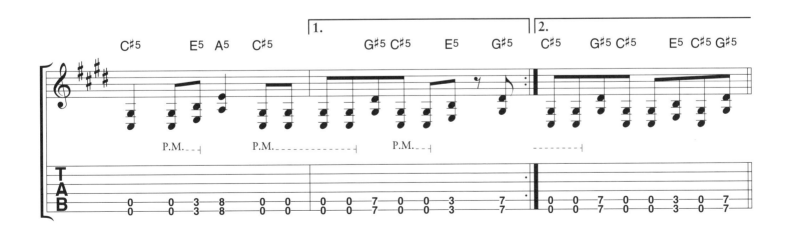

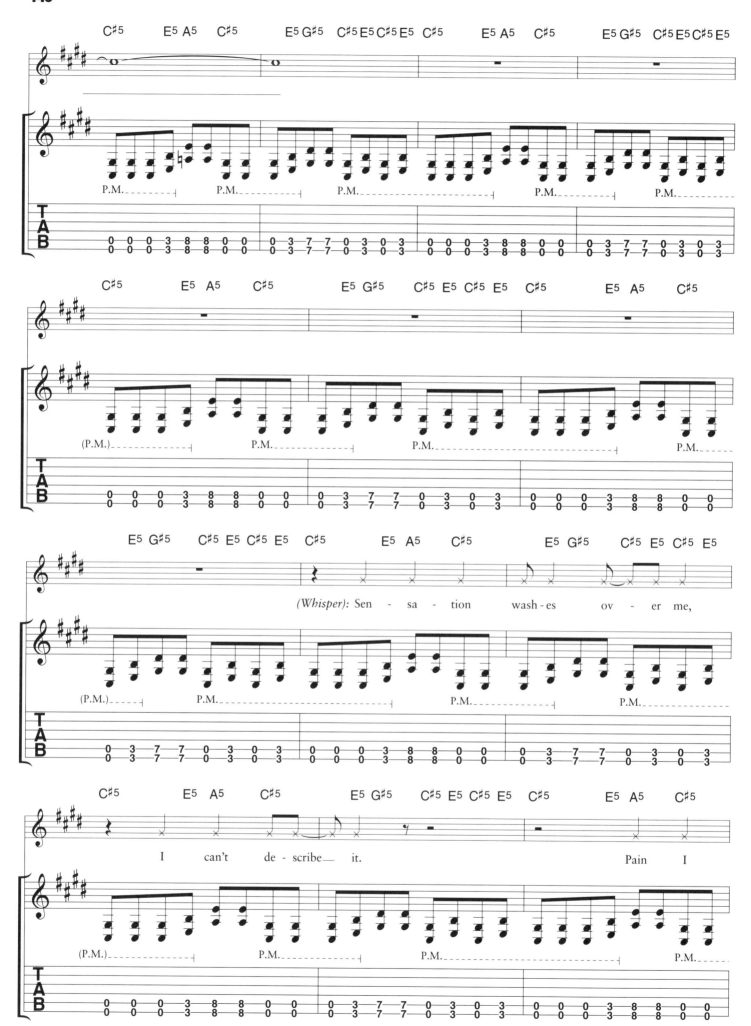

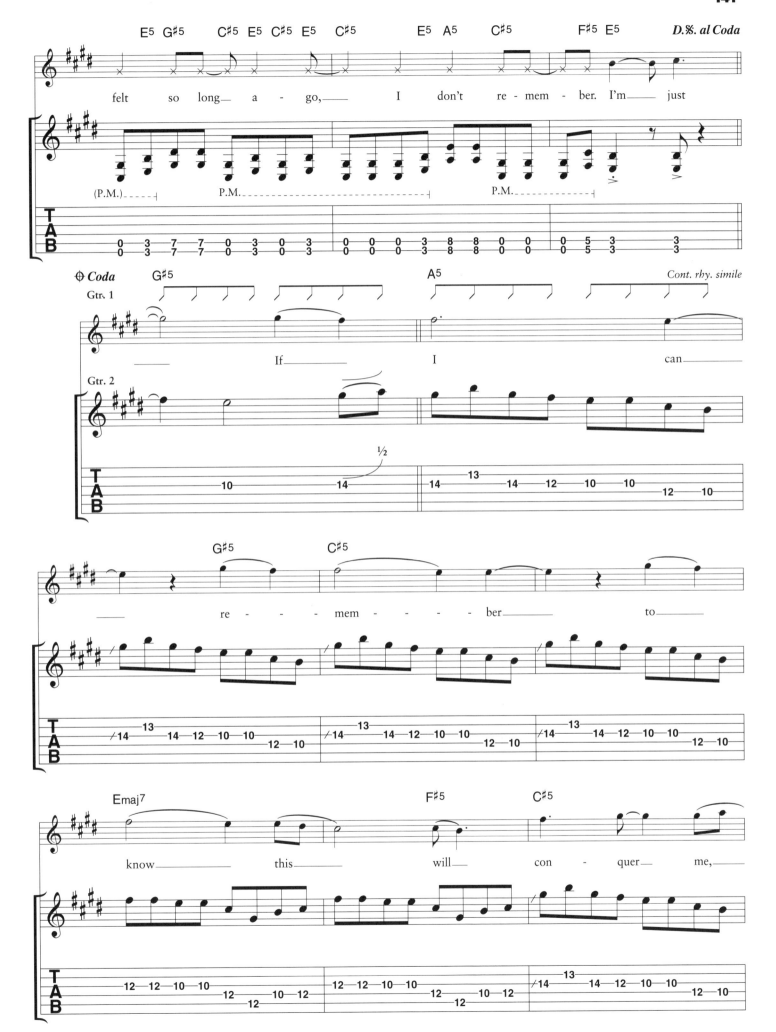

Prayer

Words and Music by Mike Wengren, Dan Donegan, David Draiman and Steve Kmak

All gtrs. tune down 1/2 step w/Drop D tuning:

⑥ = D♭   ③ = G♭
⑤ = A♭   ② = B♭
④ = D♭   ① = E♭

♩ = 98   *Intro:*

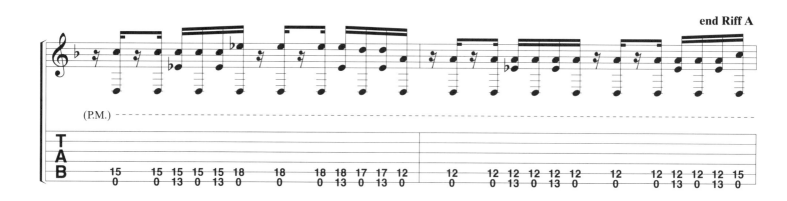

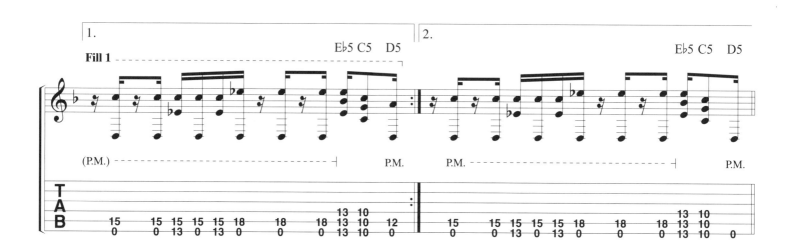

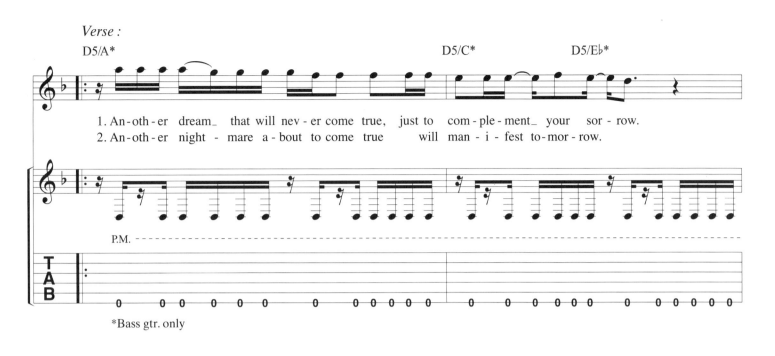

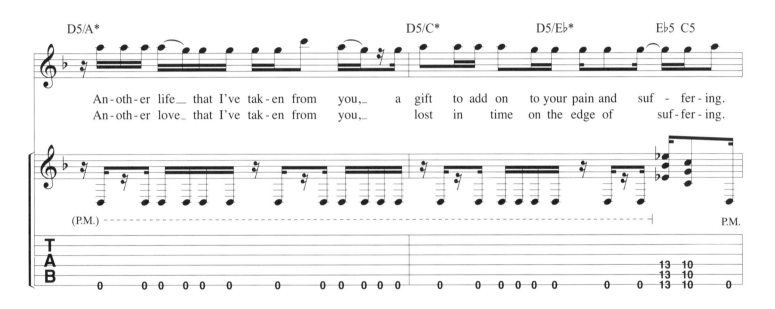

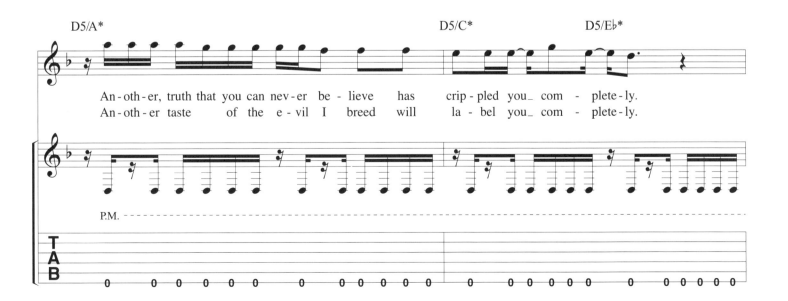

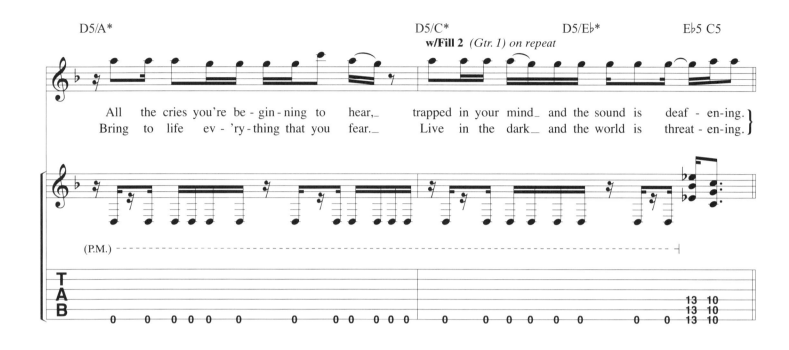

D5/A*   D5/C*   D5/Eb*   Eb5 C5

w/Fill 2 *(Gtr. 1) on repeat*

All   the cries you're be - gin - ning to   hear,__   trapped in your mind__ and the sound is   deaf - en - ing.
Bring   to life ev - 'ry - thing that you   fear.__   Live   in the dark__ and the world is   threat - en - ing.

(P.M.)

Pre-chorus:

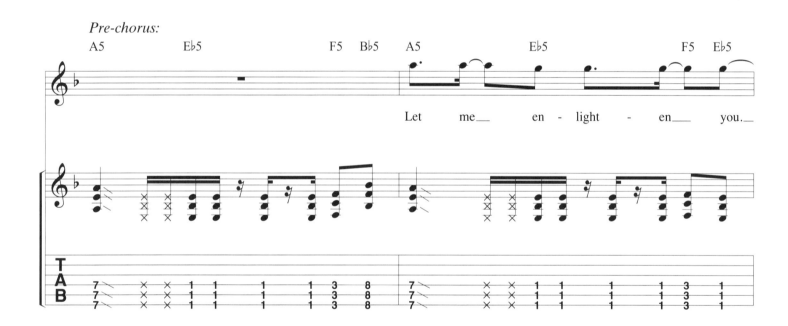

A5   Eb5   F5 Bb5 A5   Eb5   F5 Eb5

Let   me__   en - light - en__   you.__

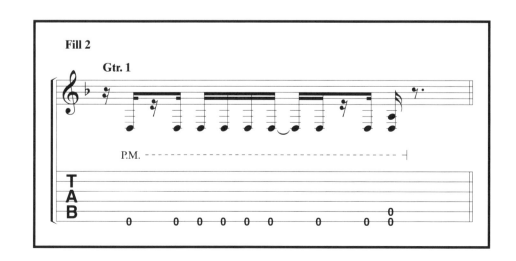

Fill 2

Gtr. 1

P.M.

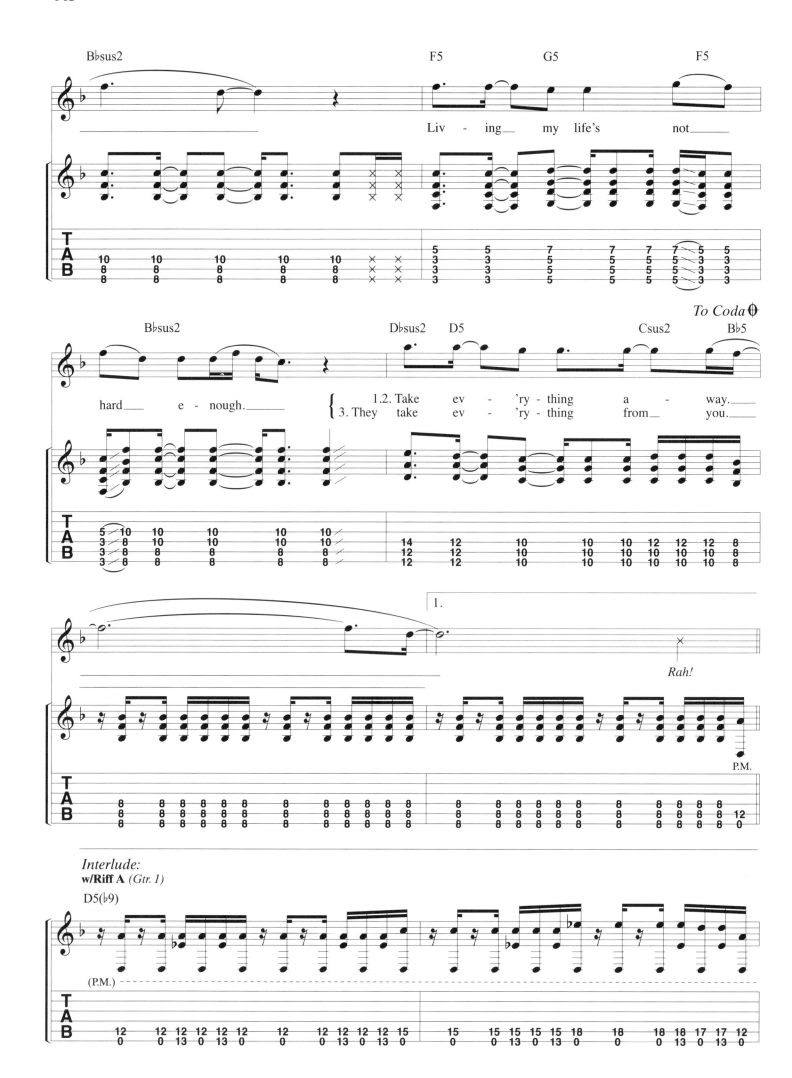

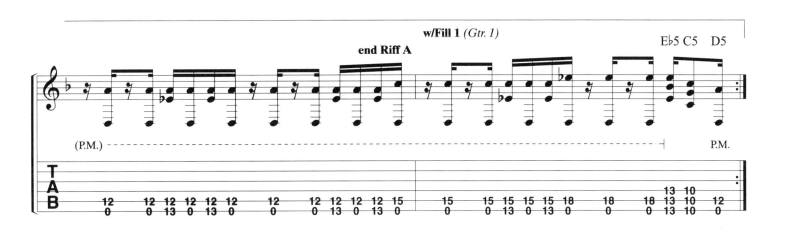

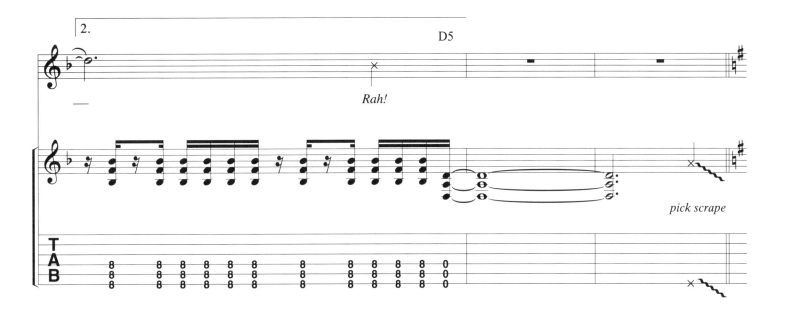

Bridge:

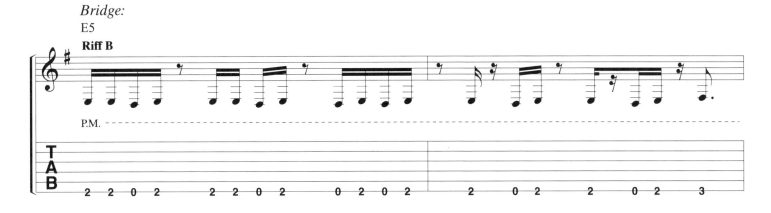

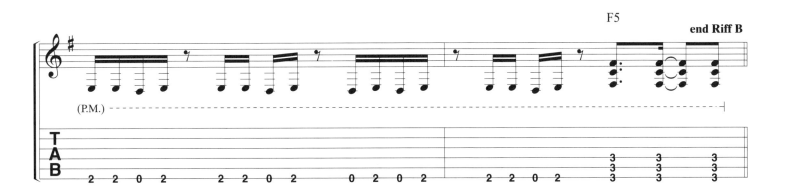

Severed

Words and Music by Chad Gray, Greg Tribbett, Matthew McDonough and Ryan Martinie

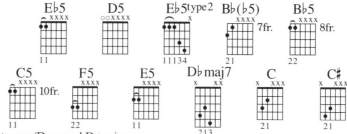

All gtrs. tune down 1 1/2 steps w/Dropped D tuning:

⑥ = B   ③ = E
⑤ = F♯   ② = G♯
④ = B   ① = C♯

Moderately ♩ = 78

Intro:

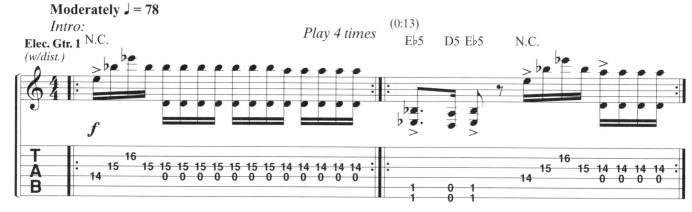

Verse 1:

And we— hide be - hind_____ lies, an - ger, hate,_ they shove_ love a - way._

___ Shells of our-selves out - side,_____ shel-ters bod - y from cold_ reigns of re - al - i - ty.

Come on, step out of your mind,___ as - sem - ble strength,

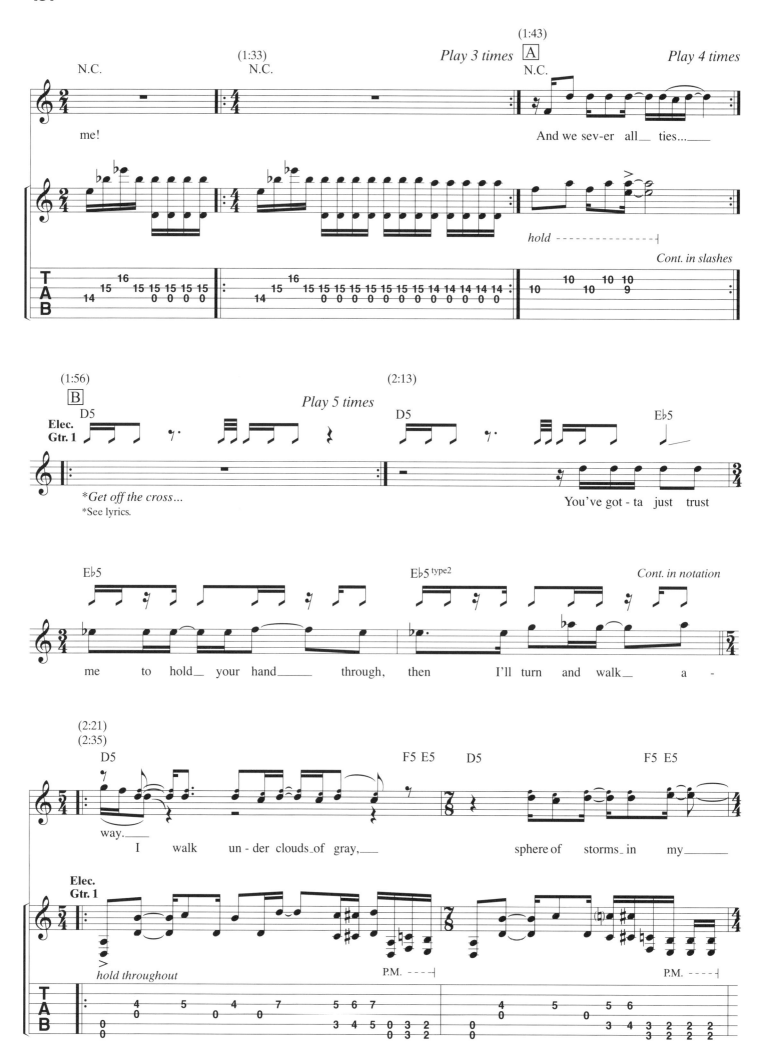

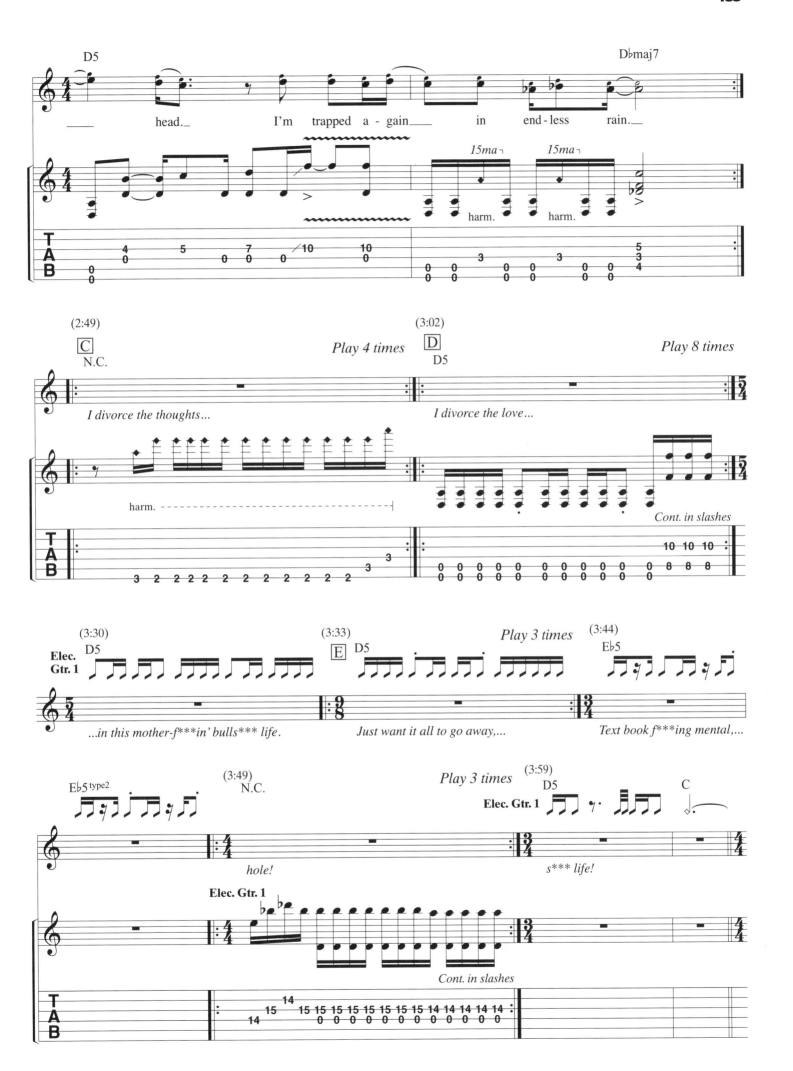

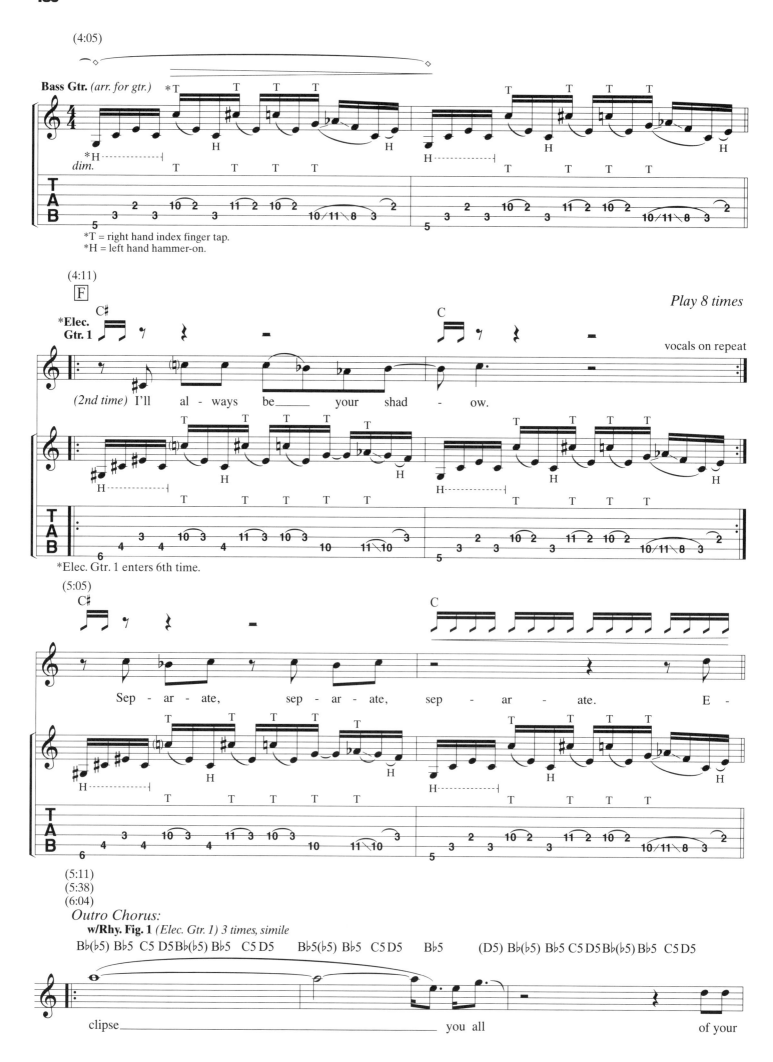

(4:05)

Bass Gtr. *(arr. for gtr.)*

*T = right hand index finger tap.
*H = left hand hammer-on.

(4:11)

F

*Elec. Gtr. 1

C♯   C

Play 8 times

vocals on repeat

(2nd time) I'll al - ways be____ your shad - ow.

*Elec. Gtr. 1 enters 6th time.

(5:05)

C♯   C

Sep - ar - ate, sep - ar - ate, sep - ar - ate. E -

(5:11)
(5:38)
(6:04)

Outro Chorus:
w/Rhy. Fig. 1 *(Elec. Gtr. 1) 3 times, simile*

B♭(♭5) B♭5 C5 D5 B♭(♭5) B♭5 C5 D5   B♭5(♭5) B♭5 C5 D5   B♭5   (D5) B♭(♭5) B♭5 C5 D5 B♭(♭5) B♭5 C5 D5

clipse_____ you all   of your

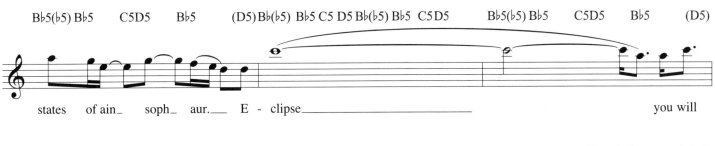

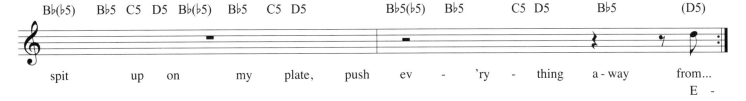

A
And we sever all ties,
It creates disruption midst circle of friends,
I become the sacrifice,
Spare your life and leave me to my misery.

B
Get off the cross, and save yourself, run away.
Run now, get away from me.
If I can get my grip, I'll pull you down into the hell I call my head.
You'll never get away.
I sit down in my ugly place and build walls out of fragments from my past
Of all the people that I needed and loved that walked away.

C
I'm trapped again in endless rain
I divorce the thoughts of you I love with me,
I divorce your innocence and my guilt,
I divorce the lying sellout confidence,
I'm divorcing every mother-f***in' thing.

D
I divorce the love bled meaningless,
I divorce the makeshift harmony,
I divorce the taunting acts of violence,
I divorce the pastime of jealousy,
I divorce control,
I divorce the faith,
I divorce the virtue,
I divorce the rain,
I divorce the excuse,
I divorce the greed,
I divorce the need,
I divorce iniquity in this mother-f***in' bulls*** life,

E
Just want it all to go away,
Just want to run away to die, take it, myself, my life.

F
I'll always be your shadow,
And veil your eyes from states of ain soph aur.
I can't be the hero anymore,
I spit up on my plate and then I turn and walk away.
I spit up on my plate and I disrupt the family,
I spit up on my plate and I sever the entity,
And I feel your warm sun on my face.

She Hates Me

Words and Music by Wesley Scantlin and Jimmy Allen

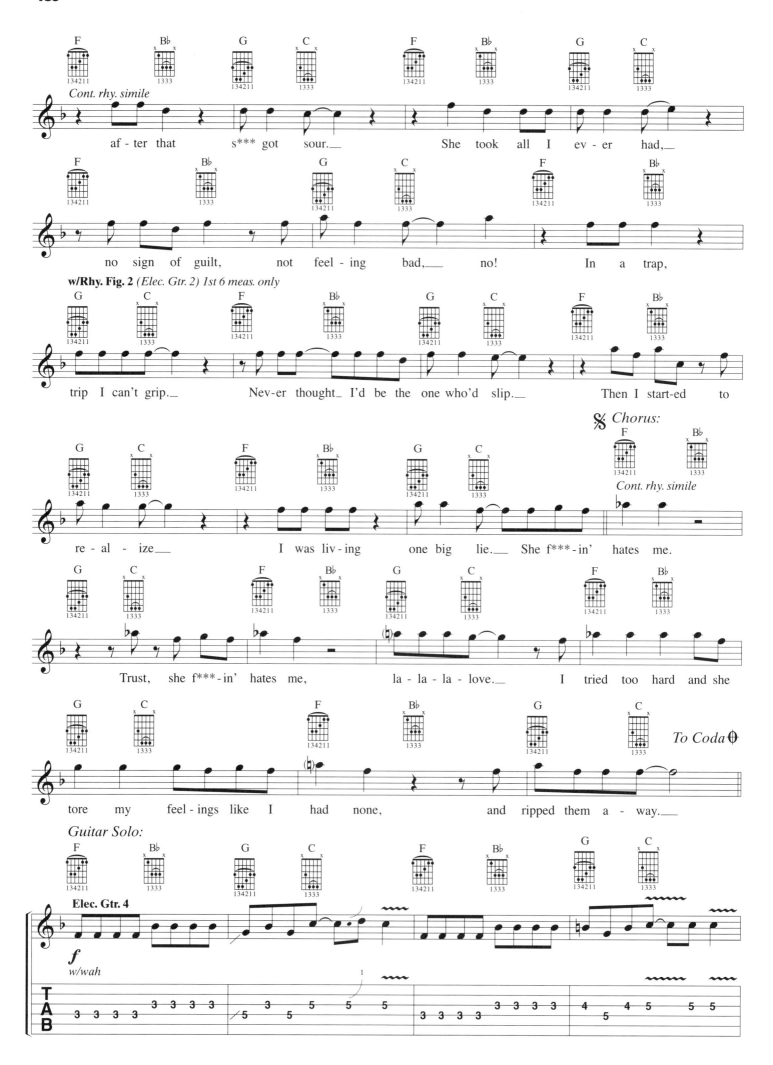

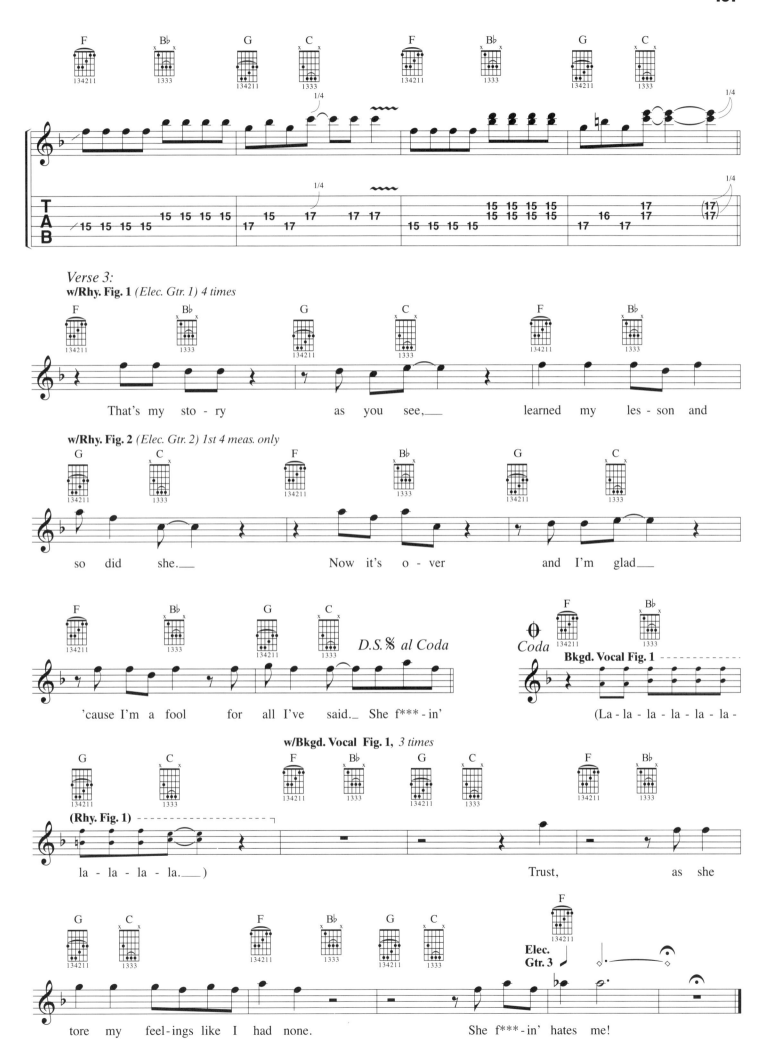

She Loves Me Not

Words and Music by Tobin Esperance, Jerry Horton Jr, Jacoby Shaddix and David Buckner

Verse 3 (Rap):
Line for line, rhyme for rhyme
Sometimes we be fighting all the goddamn time
It's makin' me sick
Relationship is gettin' ill
Piss drunk, stupid mad
On the real, could you feel
What I feel, what's the deal girl?
We're tearin' up each other's world
We should be in harmony, boy and girl
That is a promise we made
Back in the day
We told each other things wouldn't be this way
I think we should work this out
It's all right baby we can scream and shout.

Time And Time Again

Words and Music by Tobin Esperance, Jerry Horton Jr, Jacoby Shaddix and David Buckner

What I Always Wanted

Words and Music by Morgan Lander and Mercedes Lander

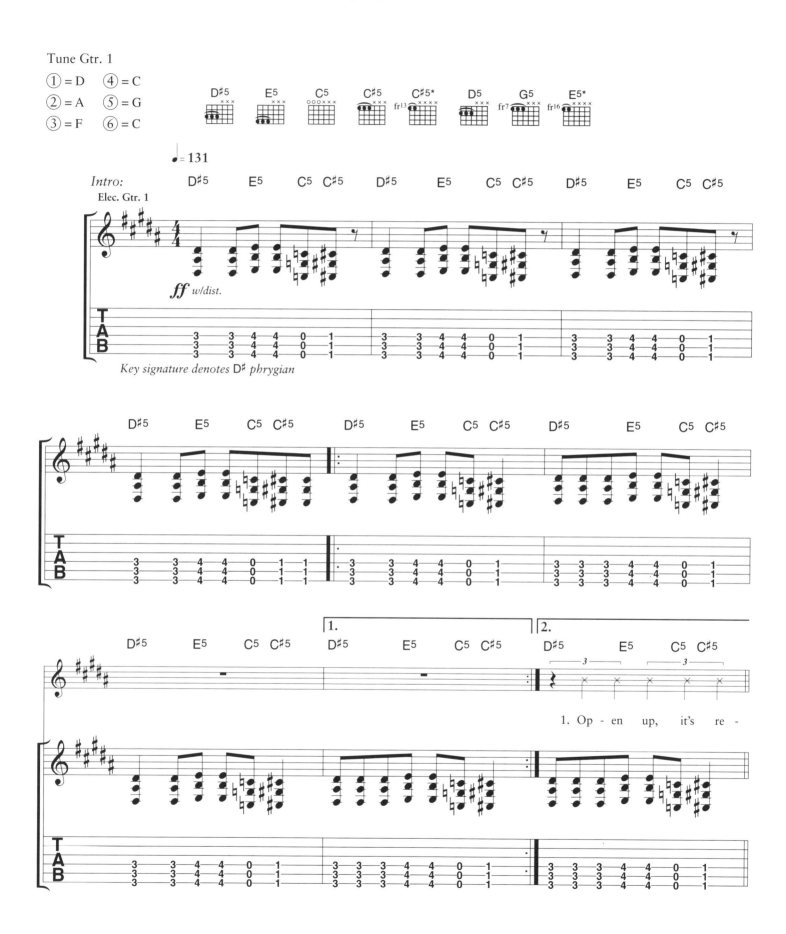

Key signature denotes D♯ phrygian

1. Op - en up, it's re -

Verse:

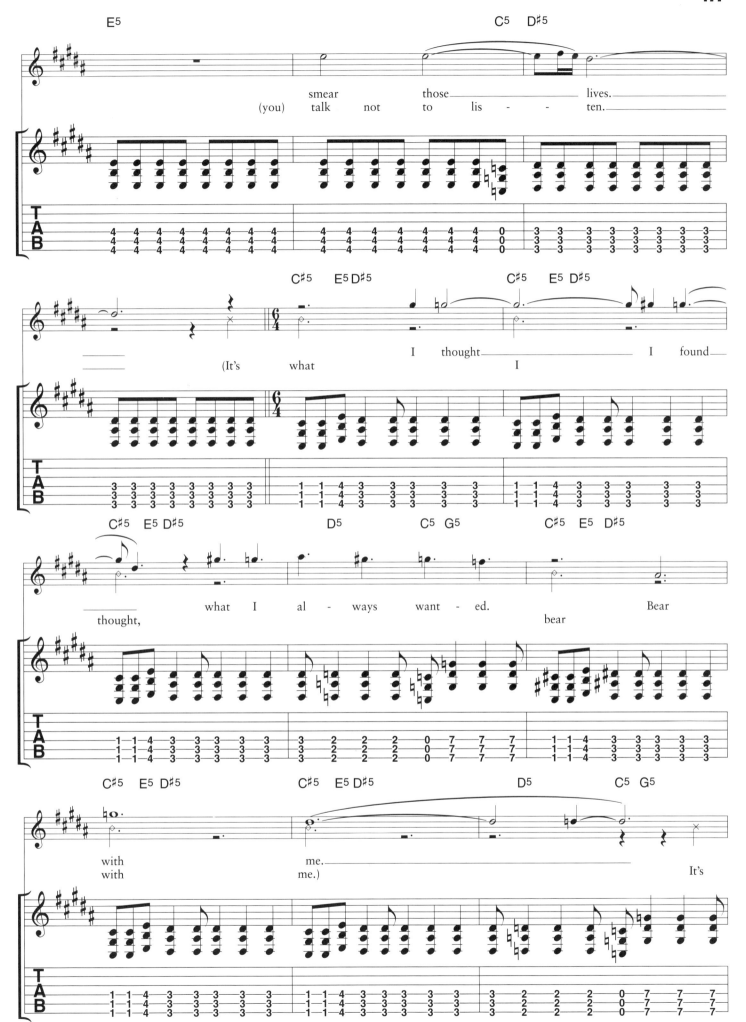

You Walk Away

Words and Music by Geno Lenardo and Richard Patrick

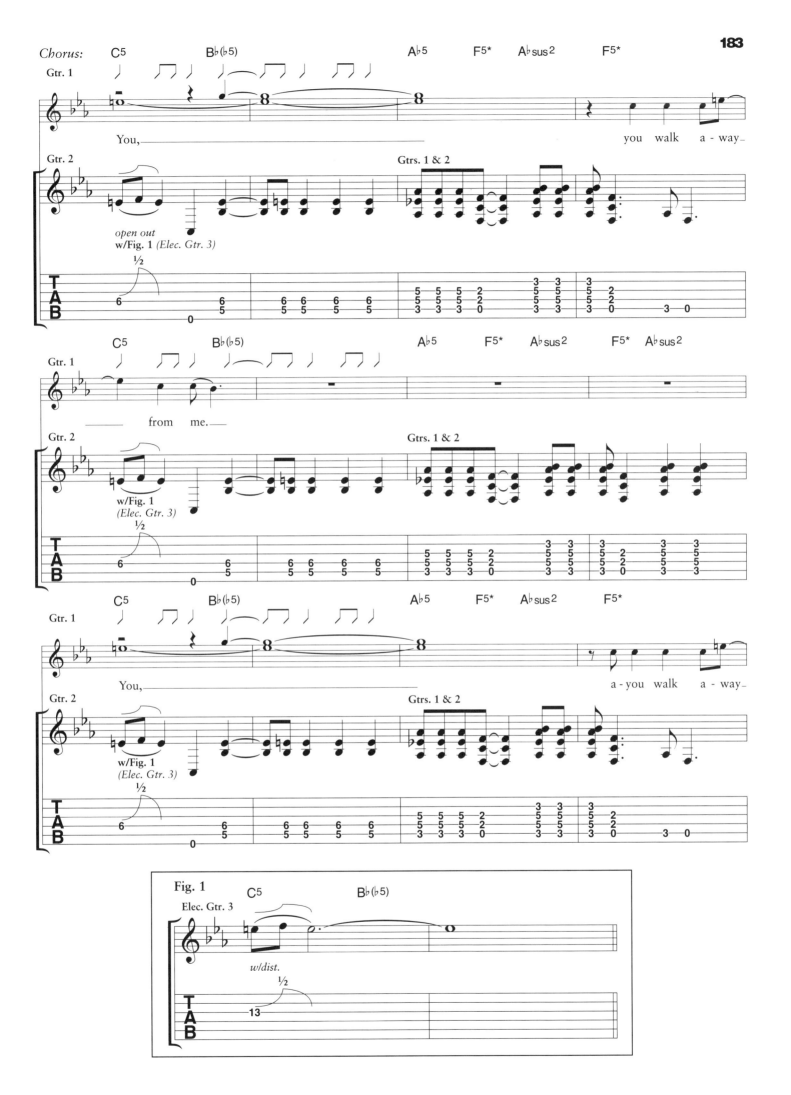

Unreal

Words and Music by Christian Machado, Dave Chavarri and Marc Rizzo

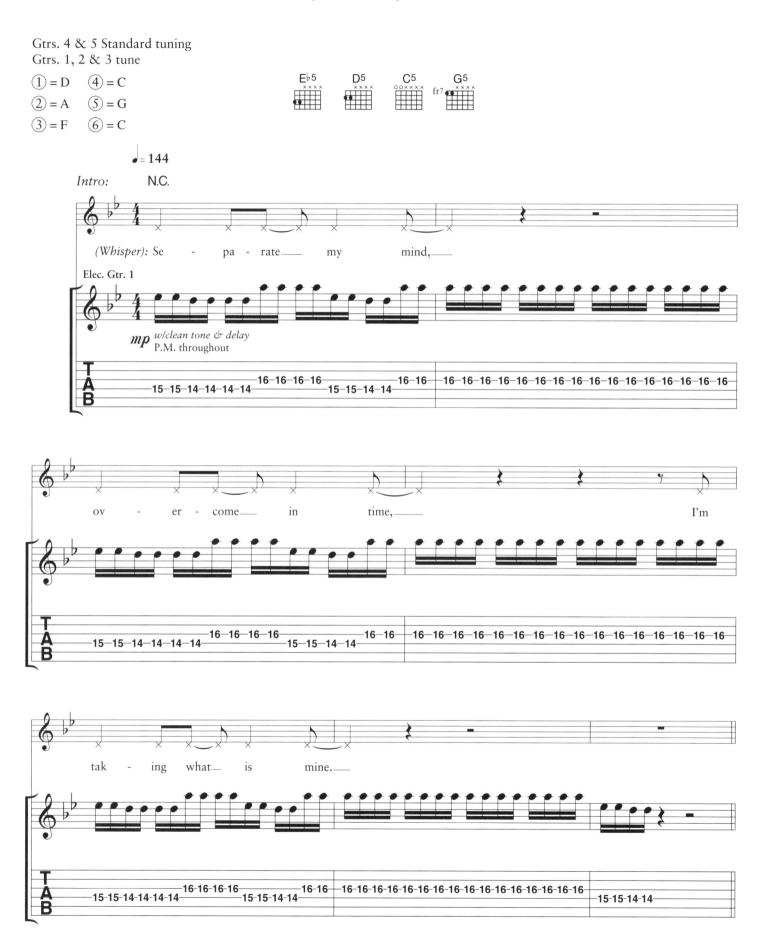

Chorus:

I don't want to shine,—
light will make us blind,— I don't want to feel—
un - real.

w/Fig. 1 *(Acous. nylon Gtr. 4) 4 times*

Elec. Gtrs. 2 & 3

Gtr. 3: w/dist.

Fig. 1

Gtr. 4 (acous. nylon)

Bridge: D5

(Whisper): Push - ing and grind - ing is twist - ing my mind frame. El tem - po que pe - sa nos

tum - ba la me - sa, y a ho - ra que es nues - tro, mi

w/**Fig. 2** *(Acous. nylon Gtr. 5)*

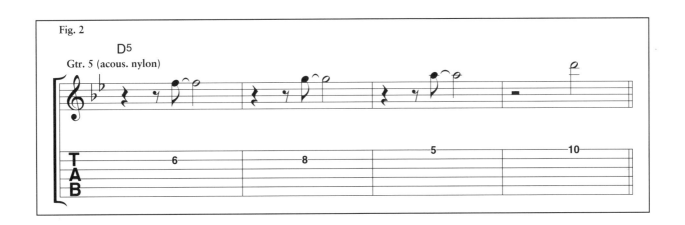

Fig. 2

D5

Gtr. 5 (acous. nylon)

D.%. al Coda